The Planets

Books by PATRICK MOORE

The Amateur Astronomer

Earth Satellites (with Irving Geis)

A Guide to the Moon

The Story of Man and the Stars

A Guide to the Stars

How to Make and Use a Telescope (with H. P. Wilkins)

The Planets

Life in the Universe (with Francis Jackson)

THE PLANETS

Patrick Moore F.R.A.S.

New York · W · W · NORTON & COMPANY · INC ·

To my Mother

Library of Congress Catalog Card No. 62-20547

PRINTED IN THE UNITED STATES OF AMERICA

Contents

Plates

Figures

FIGURES

Foreword

SINCE THE BEGINNING OF direct space exploration, in 1957, interest in our neighbour worlds – the bodies of the Solar System – has grown considerably. Yet the interest was always there; each planet has a fascination of its own.

When my book *Guide to the Planets* was published, some years ago, the idea of space exploration was still generally regarded as rather far-fetched. The situation now is very different. Moreover, there have been almost equally interesting developments in the field of pure astronomy; new techniques have been brought into use, and our knowledge is growing all the time.

Rather than produce a revision of the old text, it seemed therefore preferable to write a completely new book. Much of the original basic material has been retained, of course, but the text has been so fully revised that it has been to all intents and purposes re-written. No doubt it too will appear out of date in a few years; meanwhile, I can only hope that it will be found useful to at least some of those who read it.

I am most grateful to L. F. Ball for providing some of his splendid drawings of the planets, and to Mr W. H. Bromage for his work on the line drawings in the text.

My thanks are also due to Messrs. W. W. Norton for their work on the American edition; in particular, to Eric Swenson. I count myself fortunate that Messrs. Norton have issued the book. It is indeed pleasant to work with a firm which combines efficiency with the utmost friendliness and co-operation.

1962 June 15 PATRICK MOORE

Chapter 1

Exploring Other Worlds

'WHEN WILL MEN GO to the Moon?'

This is a question which has been asked many thousands of times since 1957 October 4, when Russian scientists opened a new era by sending up the first artificial satellite in history. So far, of course, nobody knows the answer. Some authorities believe that men will land on the Moon within the next few years; others are more cautious, and give dates ranging from 1980 to 2000; a few still doubt whether a lunar voyage will ever be possible. However, nobody is likely to dispute that the Rocket Age has well and truly arrived.

The Moon must be our first target, because it is so much closer than any other natural body in the sky. Next, presumably, will come Mars or Venus. The remaining planets in the Sun's family or 'Solar System' are more remote and even less welcoming, so that at our present stage of technical development it is rather pointless to speculate further.

Yet it would be quite wrong to suppose, as many people do, that manned interplanetary flight is the only purpose behind the space research programmes. Actually it is only one branch of the new science of astronautics, and perhaps not even the most important one. To the astronomer, sending an instrumented vehicle to Venus or Mars and bringing it safely back would be just as profitable as landing a man on the Moon.

Rocket research is still in its infancy, but telescopic astronomy is centuries old. It dates from 1609, when Galileo Galilei first turned his low-powered telescope to the skies and observed such wonders as the craters of the Moon, the four satellites of Jupiter, and the myriad stars of the Milky Way. We can explore the planets without leaving the Earth's surface at all, and it is easy to see that the Solar System is a fascinating place.

The system is made up of one star – the Sun; nine planets, including the Earth; thirty-one known moons or satellites of the planets, and various less important bodies such as comets and meteors. The Earth is by no means the largest of the planets. It has a diameter of just over 7,900 miles, but we could pack thirteen hundred globes the size of our world inside giant Jupiter and still leave room to spare.

Judged by our everyday standards, the Solar System is a large place indeed. The distance between the Earth and the Sun is 93,000,000 miles, while the outermost planet, Pluto, moves at a mean distance of some 3,666,000,000 miles from the Sun. Figures for the other planets are given in Appendix V, but meanwhile it may be helpful to imagine a scale model which is more within the range of our ordinary experience. Suppose that we reduce the Sun to a globe 600 feet in diameter, and center it in the District of Columbia. We can then work out the sizes and distances of our companion worlds:

Mercury, 2 ft. in diameter, 4¾ mi. away (in Mt. Ranier, Md.).
Venus, 5¼ ft. in diameter, 9 mi. away (in Falls Church, Va.).
Earth, 5½ ft. in diameter, 12¼ mi. away (in Mt. Vernon, Va.).
Mars, 3 ft. in diameter, 18½ mi. away (in Fort Meade, Md.).
Jupiter, 60 ft. in diameter, 64 mi. away (in Gettysburg, Pa.).
Saturn, 51 ft. in diameter, 117 mi. away (in Philadelphia).
Uranus, 22 ft. in diameter, 236 mi. away (in Youngstown, Ohio).
Neptune, 19½ ft. in diameter, 370 mi. away (in Springfield, Ohio).
Pluto, 2½ ft. in diameter, 485 mi. away (in Louisville, Ky.).

If we exclude Pluto, which presents some special problems, it will be seen that the planets fall into two distinct groups – one made up of small bodies (Mercury to Mars) and the other of giants. Between the paths or 'orbits' of Mars and Jupiter we find many thousands of dwarf worlds known as the minor planets or asteroids, represented in our scale model by small globes ranging in diameter between a millimetre and three inches.

In our exploration of the planets, the first thing is to learn how to recognize them, and fortunately this is easy enough. Venus and Jupiter are always much more brilliant than any of the stars, while Mars shines with its characteristic red colour and Saturn with a steady yellowish light. Mercury is more elusive, but may sometimes be seen low in the west after sunset or low in the east before dawn.

Uranus, Neptune and Pluto are of course. much fainter, and were discovered only in comparatively modern times.

The Moon and planets have no light of their own, and shine only because they reflect the rays of the Sun. This does not apply to the stars, which are suns in their own right, and if we try to add any of the stars to our scale model we will find ourselves in difficulty.

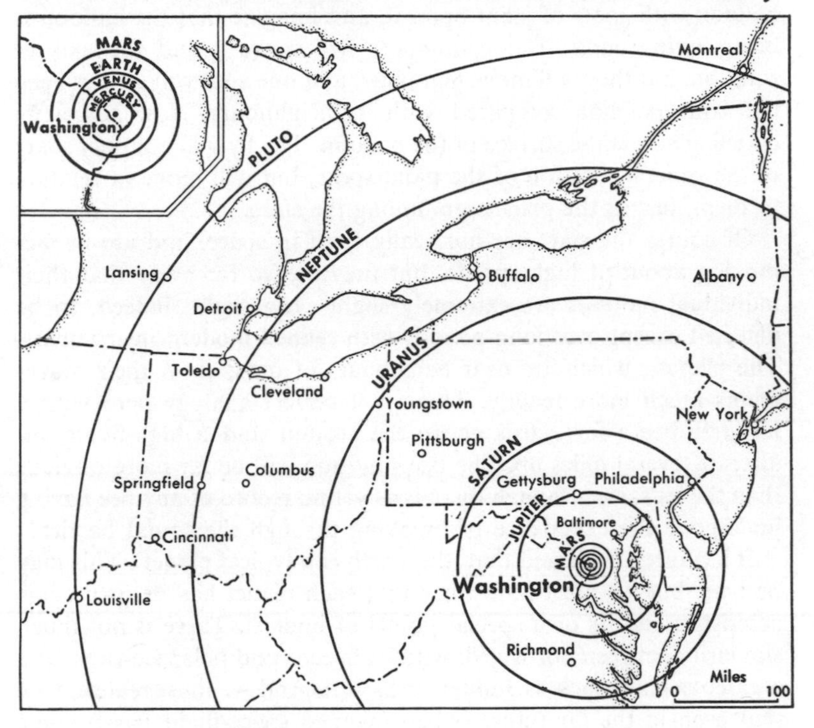

FIG. 1. The solar system to scale

Reducing the Sun to a globe only one foot in diameter, and the Earth to a small bead 36 yards away, the nearest star will lie at a distance of 5,500 miles – somewhere in Russia. The Solar System proves to be very unimportant in the universe as a whole.

Because the stars are so remote, they seem to remain almost fixed in relation to each other. Familiar constellations such as Orion and the Plough look the same now as they did in the time of Julius Cæsar. The apparent movement of the sky from east to west is due to the real rotation of the Earth on its axis, and has nothing directly to do with the stars themselves. The Sun, Moon and planets share in this general east–west movement, but in addition they have perceptible movements of their own, and seem to wander slowly about the sky. Indeed, the word 'planet' really means 'wandering star'.

A rough experiment will serve to make this quite clear. Picture a balloon with spots of paint upon it, and imagine that the balloon is being spun round. The paint-spots will move round the axis of rotation, but they will move in a mass, and one spot will always keep the same position compared with its neighbours. Now add a fly crawling across the surface of the balloon. The fly will not only share in the general rotation of the paint-spots, but will move in relation to them, just as the planets do among the stars.

Of course the stars are not really fixed in space, and are in fact moving about at high speeds, but they are so far away that their individual motions are extremely slight – too slight, indeed, to be detected except over long periods with refined modern instruments. The planets, which are near neighbours of ours, show their movements much more readily. There is a perfect analogy here with a leisurely bee a few yards above the ground and a high-flying jet-aircraft several miles up. The bee's motion will be far more obvious than the jet's, even though there is as yet no record of any bee having undergone the experience of breaking through the sound barrier!

It has often been said that 'the Earth is a typical planet'. This may be true, but we must remember that each planet has its own characteristics and its own special points of interest. There is not much similarity between our world, with its oceans and polar ice-caps, and a gaseous giant such as Jupiter or Saturn. And we must realize, too, that even in the far future, when manned space-flight has become common, our direct exploration will have to be limited to planets which are not hopelessly hostile.

Telescopic studies are not so limited, and there is much work to be done. No amateur scientist can build a space-ship, but if he has adequate instrumental equipment he can play a useful part in adding to our knowledge of our companions in the Solar System. This is important from a practical as well as a theoretical point of view. One day, no doubt, the first pioneer will land on the cloud-covered surface of Venus or the dusty desert of Mars, and the more information we can collect for him the better chance he will have of a safe return.

Chapter 2

The Birth of the Planets

THE PROBLEM OF HOW the Earth came into being is a most fascinating one, and has always intrigued the minds of men. Ancient mythology abounds with stories about the Creation; for instance, the Iroquois Indians of North America believed that 'a heavenly woman was tossed out of Heaven, and fell upon a turtle, which grew into the Earth'.

Originally the Earth was thought to be flat, and to lie in the centre of the universe. It was only when men began to have a real understanding of the Solar System, and realized that the Earth is simply one of a number of planets moving round the Sun, that real progress could be made. The problem of the birth of our own world is bound up with that of the formation of all the other planets; once we know definitely how the Earth was created, we will be well on the way to solving at least some of the mysteries of cosmical evolution.

Unfortunately, we must admit that our ideas are still rather vague. No theory yet put forward can be considered really satisfactory, though we know much more than we even suspected a few decades ago.

Perhaps the first thing to do is to work out just how old the Earth is, and here we are on comparatively safe ground. It seems highly probable that the age of the Earth is about 4,500 million years. Of course, such an enormous lapse of time is quite beyond our understanding. Recorded history carries us back some way into the past, and archæological research increases the time-span still more; but even the study of fossils, which takes us back millions of years, can only give us information about the more recent events in the Earth's life-story. The age of our planet has been estimated in various ways, one of the most useful of which depends on the behaviour of uranium.

Uranium, the heaviest of the 92 elements known to occur in

be over a thousand miles away. Two mosquitoes flying about inside the Royal Festival Hall would be far more likely to collide than any two stars. Nevertheless, it is within the bounds of possibility that some time in its history the Sun did pass dangerously close to another star; and such an encounter would have far-reaching effects, since the gravitational strain set up between the two bodies would be tremendous.

Chamberlin and Moulton supposed that as the second star approached the Sun massive tides were raised, both upon the star and upon the Sun itself, until at last a large quantity of matter was torn away from the Sun and sent spiralling around it. We can only begin to imagine the scene when the two stars were only a few million miles apart – great streamers of gas and torn-off matter circling the wounded Sun, while immense tides, augmented by Titanic eruptions within the solar globe, reached incredible violence, lessening at last as the intruder moved away.

Having done its work, the wandering star retreated into the distance, leaving the Sun surrounded by a cloud of débris. Slowly this débris cooled down and solidified into small particles or 'planetesimals'; now and then aggregations of these planetesimals formed, and in a few cases the aggregations were massive enough to collect other materials by gravitational attraction. Gradually, almost all the planetesimals were collected into a few large lumps, the final result being a system of planets.

Once an aggregation reached a diameter of a hundred miles or so, its pull would become so strong that it might grow comparatively quickly into a body of planetary dimensions. Unfortunately for the theory, it has been shown that under the conditions assumed by Chamberlin and Moulton no aggregation could ever reach sufficient size and mass for the collecting process to become possible. The high temperature of the material torn away from the Sun would make it disperse long before it could condense into planets.

Sir James Jeans, well remembered for his popular books and broadcasts as well as for his more serious works, recognized this difficulty, and put forward a modified tidal theory according to which the planets condensed out of a long, cigar-shaped filament drawn out of the Sun by the pull of the passing star. A particularly attractive feature of this idea is that it would account for the largest planets (Jupiter and Saturn) being found in the middle of the 'cigar',

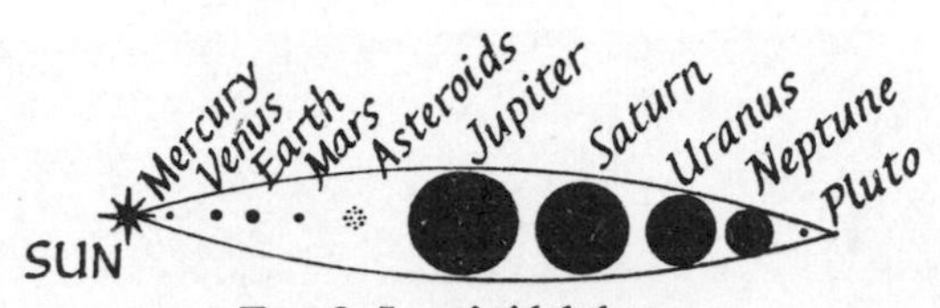

FIG. 2. Jeans' tidal theory

with the smallest planets at the tapering ends. An analogous process would account for the formation of planetary satellites, the Sun now in the disturbing rôle originally played by the passing star.

Various mathematical difficulties in Jeans' theory led Sir Harold Jeffreys to suggest that the wandering star actually struck the Sun a glancing blow. This was not a new idea, as it had been previously put forward (though in somewhat garbled form) by A. W. Bickerton, but the actual process of planet formation remained much the same as Jeans had supposed. Unfortunately, even this modification did not remove all the objections, and in some respects it made matters worse.

The death-blow to all tidal and collision theories was given by mathematical analysis, which showed that even if such processes could produce planets (which is open to doubt), these planets would have to stay close to the Sun, revolving at distances of only a few million miles. It would be impossible to have a planet even as far out as Mercury (36,000,000 miles), to say nothing of remote Uranus or Neptune. There seems to be no way round this obstacle, and all we can do is to start thinking along different lines.

Jeans calculated that on an average, any particular star would pass close by another only once in every 500,000 million million years. His figures have been questioned, but stellar encounters are certainly very rare, and relatively few stars will have experienced them in their life-histories. However, it would be wrong to suppose that each star is a solitary wanderer in space.

Nearly everyone is familiar with the constellation known as the Big Dipper. The second star in the Dipper's handle is Mizar, easily identifiable because a much fainter star, Alcor, lies close beside it. When a telescope is used, Mizar itself appears as two stars, so close together that to the unaided eye they appear as a single mass. This is no mere perspective effect; the two stars really are associated, and revolve round their common centre of gravity much as the two bells

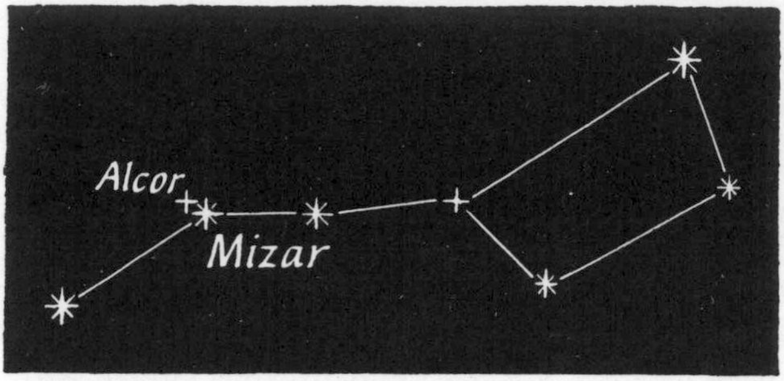

FIG. 3. The Big Dipper

of a dumb-bell move when twisted by the joining arm. They form what is known as a 'binary' or double-star system.[1]

Binary pairs are very common, and attempts have been made to account for the Sun's system of planets by supposing that the Sun itself was formerly one component of a binary. For instance, H. N. Russell suggested that it was the companion star which was struck by the intruder, giving rise to enough débris to account for the planets; R. A. Lyttleton considered that the near approach of the wandering star might be enough to wrench the binary companion away from the Sun's sphere of influence, planet-forming matter being scattered in the process. Perhaps the most ingenious variation of the binary theory, however, was proposed by F. Hoyle, who dispensed with the intruding star altogether.

According to Hoyle, the Sun was originally one member of a binary system, the companion being about as far away from it as Jupiter is at present (in the region of 500,000,000 miles). The Sun was a perfectly ordinary star, but the companion was not. Several thousands of millions of years ago, it exploded with a catastrophic blaze of light and heat which equalled the combined radiation of all the other stars in our Galaxy put together. We know that such stellar outbursts do occur now and then. They are known as 'supernovæ', and can be seen across space over distances of thousands of millions of light-years.[2]

[1] The system of Mizar is actually more complicated than this, but there are many binary systems which consist simply of two stars almost identical in size and mass.

[2] A light-year is the distance travelled by a ray of light in one year: about 5,880,000,000,000 miles. The nearest of the so-called 'fixed stars', Proxima Centauri, lies at a distance of slightly over 4 light-years from us.

In a supernova explosion, most of the star's material is hurled out into space, and the whole outburst lasts for only a few days, so that the energy generated is tremendous. Hoyle calculated that one of the effects of the explosion would be to give what was left of the star a recoil sufficient to break its gravitational connection with the Sun. During the last stages of its outburst, probably as it started its outward journey, the companion ejected a relatively small quantity of material which the Sun managed to retain. The planets then condensed out of this material rather in the way which Chamberlin and Moulton had supposed in their original planetesimal theory – only this time conditions would be less unfavourable for the formation of large lumps of matter.

If the theory is correct, the original companion star may still be visible to us, even though we cannot recognize it. According to modern ideas, a supernova does not destroy itself completely; from being a massive star of enormous dimensions it collapses into a special type of star known as a white dwarf, of small size (comparable with that of a planet) and a density so great that a thimbleful of white dwarf material would weigh hundreds of tons. There are plenty of white dwarfs in our part of the Galaxy, and one of these could well be the Sun's erstwhile attendant.

Unfortunately the whole supernova idea is very difficult to prove or disprove. It has not met with a great deal of support, but at least there are no obvious fatal objections to it, and it remains an intriguing possibility.

Oddly enough, we are slightly more confident about the birth of the Sun and other stars than we are about that of the Earth. The stars appear to have condensed out of 'nebulæ', clouds of gas and dust in space; many of these nebulæ are known, the most famous example being that of Orion's Sword. There is no reason to suppose that the birth-process of the Sun was in any way exceptional.

Binaries, as we have seen, are very common. Sometimes the two components are roughly similar in mass, as with Mizar, but in other cases one member of the pair is much more massive than the other, with a ratio of at least 10 to 1. It is generally thought that the two components are born separately, relatively close to each other inside the nebula.

This has led on to another interesting theory, due to G. P. Kuiper of the United States. Kuiper regards the Solar System as a degenerate binary in which the second mass did not condense into a single body, but was spread out. Instead of two stars, one with ten times the mass of the other, the initial result was one star (the Sun) attended by a number of condensations or 'protoplanets'. The total mass of the protoplanets would amount to about one-tenth the mass of the Sun. Once formed, the protoplanets would contract to form the planets which we know, while most of the original solar cloud would be lost to interstellar space.

Here again we have an idea which is quite plausible, but we may be completely wrong in supposing that the Solar System is the result of a binary – degenerate or otherwise. Entirely different theories have been put forward by O. Schmidt, in Russia, and C. von Weizsäcker, in Germany. Their hypotheses differ markedly in detail, but have basic points of similarity, and mark something of a return to Laplace's old Nebular Hypothesis, though in vastly improved form.

This time it is supposed that the Sun once passed through a nebula, or at least a region containing an appreciable quantity of gas and dust, and that it collected an extensive 'envelope' of material. Upon emerging from the nebula, the Sun was thus left with a tenuous shell extending out further than the present orbit of Neptune, the outermost of the large planets. Collisions and friction between the particles of the material resulted in the formation of a circular, disk-shaped shell. As time passed, gravitational effects created aggregations of matter; when these became massive enough, they drew in yet more matter, so that planets were built up. Once again we have an accretion process, but this time we can dispense with the intruding star of Jeans and Jeffreys, the cosmic disaster suggested by Hoyle, Kuiper's degenerate binary, and the impossible gaseous rings of Laplace.

Theories of this sort have received wide support. Modifications of them have been proposed recently – notably by H. Alfvén, who believes that magnetic forces played a major rôle in the building-up of planets from the solar cloud. Yet so far we cannot pretend to be certain about anything, and a tremendous amount of work remains to be done.

One interesting fact should be borne in mind. Collisions between two stars are very infrequent, and even supernovæ are rare, so that if we follow Jeans or Hoyle we must regard Solar Systems as true galactic freaks. But interstellar clouds are common enough; and if we accept a theory of the type suggested by Schmidt, von Weizsäcker or Alfvén, it is probable that systems of planets are far from rare in the universe.

If we could look back thousands of millions of years in time, we would find ourselves confronted with a very strange picture; a young Sun, still newly born out of the nebular matter, unaccompanied by the familiar planets which we know, but perhaps surrounded by an extensive gaseous shell, or lying within range of the companion star which was later to sear its fellow with light and heat beyond all understanding. But what of the future?

We are wholly dependent upon the Sun. Our existence in the universe depends on the constancy of solar radiation, and any marked increase or withdrawal of the Sun's energy would be fatal to us. We manage to survive because conditions are just right for us, but this state of things will not continue indefinitely.

It was formerly believed that the Sun was gradually cooling down, and that all life on Earth would eventually be frozen to death, but this view is now known to be wrong. As the Sun ages, it is growing steadily more luminous. In the far future, many thousands of millions of years ahead yet, the oceans will boil, the atmosphere will escape into space, and all earthly things, from the descendants of men (if any survive) down to the lowliest plants, will perish. This state of affairs will not last for long on the cosmical scale, for the Sun's blaze will be its last defiant gesture of departing glory. Subsequently it will collapse into a small massive body, well on the road to its own end; at last it will reach its final condition as a cold, dark globe, lightless and heatless, still accompanied by its remaining planets. But this will not concern us – for we will not be there to see. In the remote past, the Sun was responsible for the creation of the Earth; in the end, it must inevitably destroy all life upon our world.

Chapter 3

The Movements of the Planets

ASTRONOMY IS THE OLDEST of all the sciences. Of course, even our earliest cave-dwelling ancestors must have looked up into the skies and wondered at what they saw there, but this was mere 'star-gazing', and can hardly be counted as true astronomy. Yet more scientific studies began at a surprisingly early date, particularly by the Chinese and the Egyptians, and there is excellent evidence that an eclipse of the Moon was intelligently observed as long ago as 1136 B.C.

On the other hand, the Chinese and the Egyptians were content to watch without asking 'why' or 'how', and it was left to the Greeks to put astronomical science on a really firm footing.

The story of Greek astronomy begins with the birth of Thales of Miletus in 624 B.C., and virtually ends with the death of Ptolemy of Alexandria about A.D. 180, so that it extends over a period of some eight centuries. This was quite long enough to result in a complete revolution in outlook, and we must agree that some of the Greek ideas were amazingly accurate. They soon realized that instead of being flat, as the cave-men thought,[1] the Earth is spherical. Later, Eratosthenes of Cyrene measured the Earth's circumference so precisely that his value was more correct than that adopted by Christopher Columbus on his voyage of discovery to the New World so many years afterwards.

Pythagoras, the great geometer who lived some 500 years before Christ, was one of the first to state that the Earth is a globe. Yet Pythagoras, like most of the other Greeks, made one mistake which was to have far-reaching effects. He believed that our world lay in the centre of the universe, with everything in the sky revolving around it.

This was natural enough – at the time; but as the apparent motions of the planets were measured with greater and greater exactness, doubts began to creep in. Finally Aristarchus of Samos, one of the

[1] And as the earnest members of the International Flat Earth Society still think!

most clear-minded of the Greek philosophers, put forward the theory that instead of the Sun going round the Earth, the Earth goes round the Sun.

This was revolutionary indeed, and even the enlightened Greeks were not ready for it. The idea that the Earth might not, after all, be the supreme body in the cosmos struck them as being heretical and dangerous. Aristarchus found few supporters, and his successors went back to the idea of a central Earth.

The most complete system of this type was described by Ptolemy of Alexandria, last of the great philosophers of the Greek school.

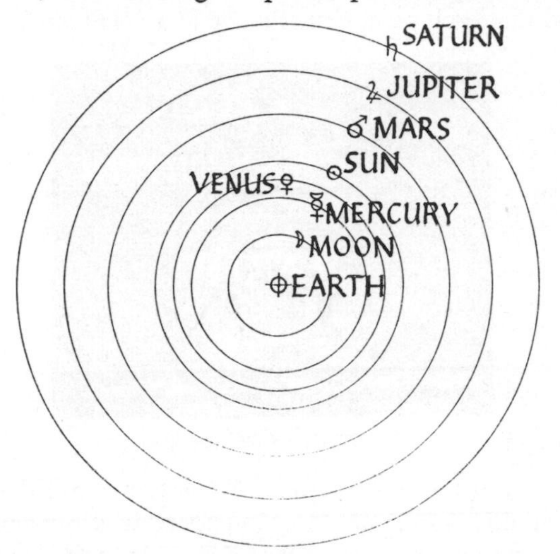

FIG. 4. The Ptolemaic System

Ptolemy himself was not primarily responsible for it, but he certainly perfected it, and wrote it all down in a book which has come to us across the ages by way of its Arab translation. It is known as the *Almagest*, and it has given us much of our information about the state of astronomy in Classical times.

According to Ptolemy, the Earth lay at rest in the centre of the universe, while the Moon, Sun, planets, and stars circled round it at various distances. 'Circled' is an apt term, since the ancients believed the circle to be the perfect form – and surely nothing short of perfection could be allowed in the heavens?

The trouble was that the movements of the planets in the sky were not in accord with uniform motion round the Earth in exactly circular paths. Mars, Jupiter and Saturn, for instance, seemed to describe slow 'loops', and for periods they seemed to travel in a backwards or *retrograde* manner among the stars. Ptolemy, who was an excellent mathematician, knew this quite well. Moreover he was in possession of a good star catalogue, and his measures of planetary positions were remarkably good considering that they had to be made without the help of a telescope.

Some sort of solution had to be found, and unfortunately Ptolemy adopted the wrong one. Rather than abandon his perfect circles, he maintained that each planet must move in a small circle or *epicycle*,

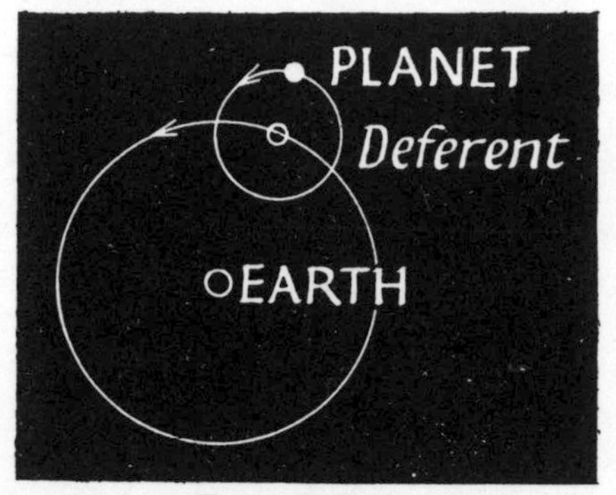

FIG. 5. Epicycles

the centre of which (the *deferent*) itself moved round the Earth in a circle. Even this would not do, and there was no choice but to introduce more and more epicycles. Finally the theory more or less fitted the apparent motions of the planets, but it had become hopelessly clumsy and artificial.

Ptolemy's ideas were accepted for more than a thousand years after his death. Even in the Middle Ages, the proposal to dethrone the Earth from its proud central position was regarded with horror. Then, in the mid-sixteenth century, the Polish canon Copernicus re-examined the whole problem, and published a book which led to the overthrow of the Ptolemaic System. The book was called *De Revolutionibus Orbium Cœlestium*, and it proved to be a landmark in scientific history.

Copernicus was by no means correct in all he said. He still kept to the idea of perfect circles, and he was even reduced to bringing back Ptolemy's epicycles. Yet he made the one great fundamental advance which was needed; he removed the Earth from the centre of the Solar System, and put the Sun there instead. Instead of being the supreme body, our world became a perfectly normal planet.

The Christian Church was bitterly opposed to anything of the kind. Copernicus knew that he would be in danger of persecution, and so he refused to publish his book until the very end of his life. Later 'heretics' were less prudent. In 1600 Giordano Bruno was burned at the stake in Rome, one of his crimes being that he taught the Copernican theory rather than the Ptolemaic.

The appearance of Copernicus' book started arguments which were to rage for over a hundred years. Oddly enough, the man responsible for the next major advance – the Danish astronomer Tycho Brahe – was no supporter of Copernicus; he stoutly maintained that the Sun must move round the Earth, and nothing would shake his belief. However, he made a great many accurate observations of star positions, and also paid close attention to the apparent motions of the planets. When he died, in 1601, he left all his results in the hands of his assistant, a young German mathematician named Johannes Kepler. Kepler used them well – but with a result quite different from anything which Tycho could have expected.

Kepler started with the assumption that the Sun must lie in the centre of the Solar System. He then did his best to work out a theory which would suit Tycho's observations. He concentrated upon Mars, and worked away for several years, only to meet with failure after failure. The observations nearly fitted, but not quite. Either Tycho's work was inaccurate, or else there was something badly wrong with the theory.

Kepler had implicit faith in Tycho as an observer, and at last he found the cause of the trouble. The planets do indeed move round the Sun, but they do so in paths or *orbits* which are not circles, but ellipses.

One way to draw an ellipse is to stick two pins in a board, an inch or two apart, and join them with a thread, leaving a certain amount of slack. Now draw the thread tight with a pencil, and trace a curve. The result will be an ellipse, the two pins marking the *foci.* If the pins are wider apart, with the same length of thread, the ellipse will be long and narrow. The distance between the foci is thus a measure of the eccentricity of the ellipse.

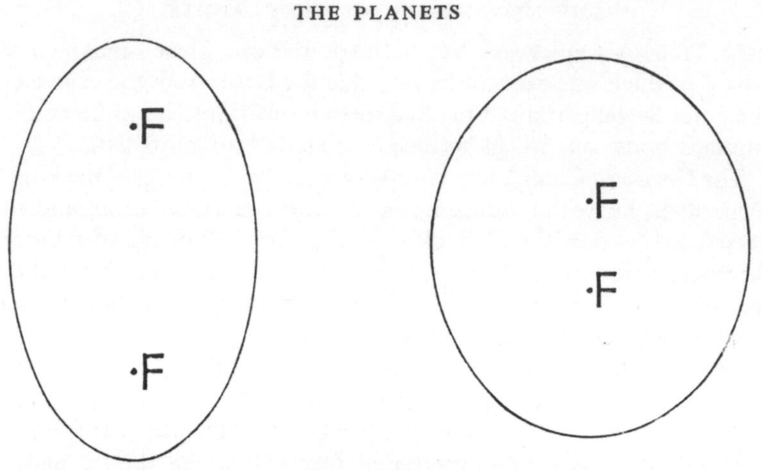

FIG. 6. Ellipses

In the case of the Earth, the Sun occupies one focus of the ellipse, while the other focus is empty. The eccentricity is low, so that the Earth's distance from the Sun never varies by much more than 1½ million miles from its average value of approximately 93 million miles. Most of the other planets, too, have orbits which are practically circular. Yet it was these slight departures from circular form which led Kepler to decide against Ptolemy's theory.

Mars has an orbit which is rather more eccentric than that of the Earth; its distance from the Sun varies between 128½ million miles at its closest or *perihelion*, and 154½ million miles at its farthest or *aphelion*. It is therefore lucky that Kepler devoted most of his attention to it. Had the path of Mars been as nearly circular as that of (say) Venus, it would have taken him much longer to find the answer to his problem.

Kepler was able to draw up three fundamental laws of planetary motion. The first stated simply that a planet moves round the Sun in an ellipse, with the Sun in one focus. The second stated that the *radius vector* sweeps out equal areas in equal times, while the third gave a relationship between a planet's time of revolution, or *sidereal period*, and its distance from the Sun.

The second law is worth a little further explanation. The radius vector is the line joining the centre of the planet to the centre of the Sun, and in the diagram the shaded area is equal to the dotted area – it being assumed that the planet takes the same time to move from

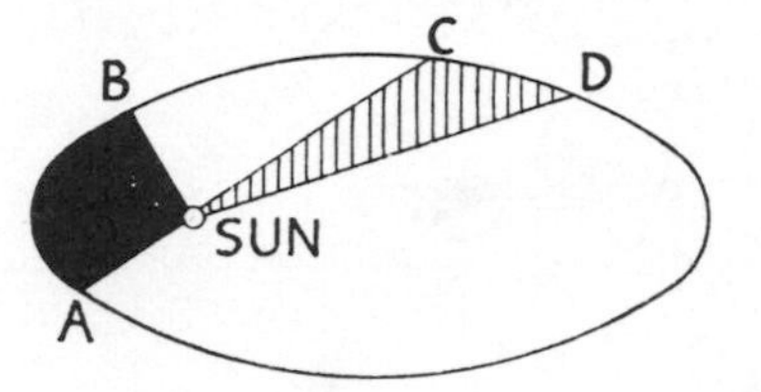

FIG. 7. Kepler's Second Law

A to B as it does from C to D. In fact, a planet moves at its quickest when near perihelion. It follows that the nearer planets are the faster-moving. Mercury travels at a mean rate of 30 miles per second; the Earth at 18½; Jupiter at 8, while Pluto, the tortoise of the Solar System, has an average velocity of only 3 miles per second.

Two of the planets, Mercury and Venus, are closer to the Sun than we are, so that they have their own way of behaving. To begin with, we can never see them against a dark background except when they are low down in the sky. They are always in roughly the same direction as the Sun, and are at their brightest when in the west after sunset or in the east before dawn. Moreover, they show phases similar to those of the Moon. The diagram here shows what happens.

Let us consider Mercury first. When in position 1, it has its dark side turned towards us, and is 'new', so that it cannot be seen at all. This is known as *Inferior Conjunction.* As it moves along in its orbit, a little of the daylight side begins to be turned in our direction, so that Mercury becomes successively a crescent, a half (*dichotomy*) at position 2, three-quarters or *gibbous*, and full at position 3. At full, or *Superior Conjunction*, it is almost behind the Sun in the sky, so that it is difficult to see even with a telescope. After superior conjunction, the phases are repeated in the reverse order; gibbous, half at position 4, and then back to new. When an evening star, Mercury is on the wane; when a morning star, it is waxing.

It is clear that there are observational difficulties to be faced. Mercury is new when at its closest to the Earth, and as the phase increases so the apparent diameter shrinks. Moreover, it is a small world, not much larger than the Moon, and never rises long before the Sun or sets long after it. City-dwellers will probably never see it with the naked eye, though at times people who live away from artificial lights may see it shining as a fairly bright, slightly pinkish starlike point.

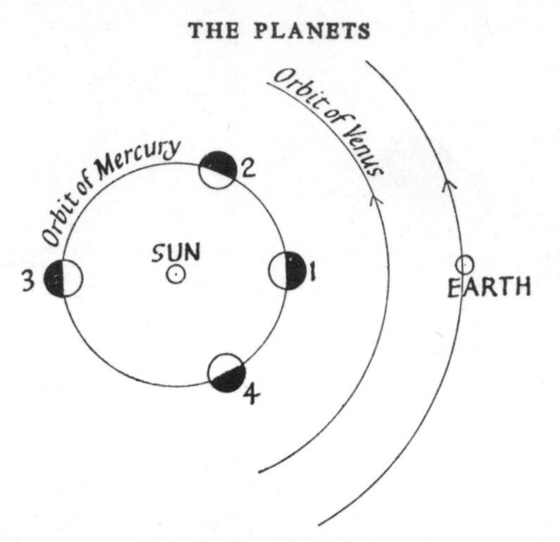

FIG. 8. Phases of Mercury

At some inferior conjunctions Mercury passes directly between the Sun and the Earth, and is then visible as a black spot in transit against the solar disk. This last happened in November 1960. It does not occur at every inferior conjunction simply because Mercury's orbit is tilted to that of the Earth, and usually the lining-up is not exact.

Venus behaves in the same way as Mercury, but is a much more conspicuous object, partly because it is larger and more reflective and partly because it is closer to us. Transits are very rare, and the next will not take place until the year 2004.

The remaining planets lie beyond the orbit of the Earth in the Solar System, and are therefore more convenient to observe. Mars, shown in the diagram, may be taken as a typical case.

Obviously, no planet outside the Earth's orbit can ever undergo inferior conjunction, since it can never pass between the Sun and the Earth. At the corresponding position in its orbit, Mars, at M1, is certainly lined up with the Sun and Earth; but this time the Earth is in the middle, with Mars opposite to the Sun in the sky and consequently well placed for observation. This is termed *opposition*, and for Mars occurs about every 780 days. To a Martian observer, the Earth would then appear to be at inferior conjunction.

Like Mercury and Venus, Mars and the outer planets can pass into superior conjunction. In this position, Mars is almost behind the Sun as seen from the Earth, and is above the horizon only during the hours of daylight.

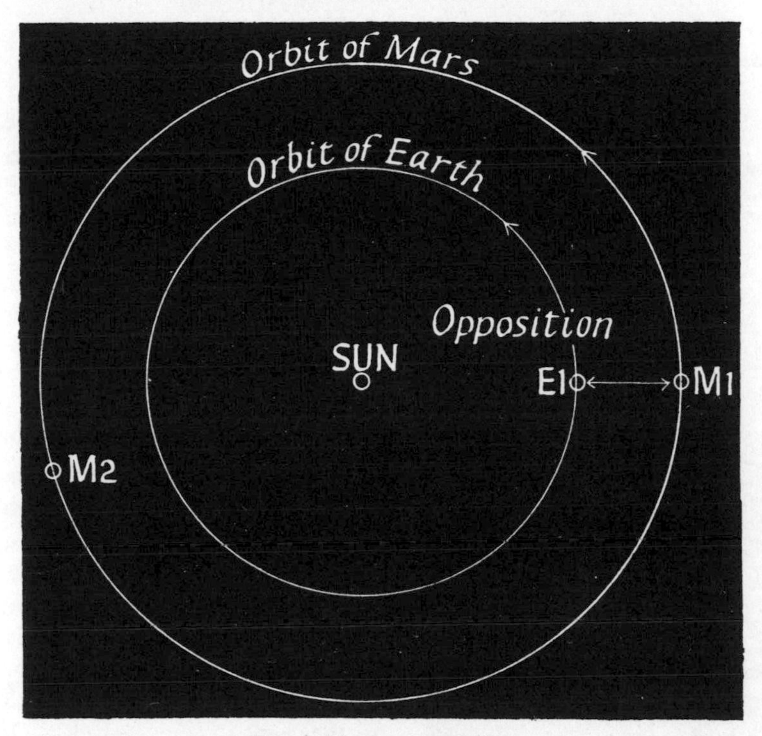

FIG. 9. Movements of Mars

The reason why Mars comes to opposition only once in 780 days or so is because both it and the Earth are moving. The Earth takes approximately 365 days to make one complete revolution round the Sun, and if we start with the Earth at E1 and Mars at M1, the Earth will have returned to its original position after 365 days. Mars, however, has a longer sidereal period – 687 days – and will not have arrived back at M1. It will have travelled only as far as M2. The Earth has to catch it up, so that we can see Mars at its best only at fairly long intervals; thus there will be oppositions in 1963, 1965, and 1967, but none in 1962, 1964, or 1966. The interval between successive oppositions is known as the planet's *synodic period.*

Conditions are not quite the same for the more distant planets. They move so slowly compared with the Earth that they are much easier to catch up. Consequently, Jupiter and the other giants, as well as Pluto, have shorter synodic periods, and come to opposition at intervals of little over a year.

We are now in a position to explain the periodical backwards or retrograde movements of Mars and other planets. In the diagram, the apparent motion in the sky is shown, together with the relative positions of the Earth and Mars in their orbits. Between positions 3 and 6, the Earth is catching up Mars and passing it, so that for some time Mars seems to retrace its steps among the stars.

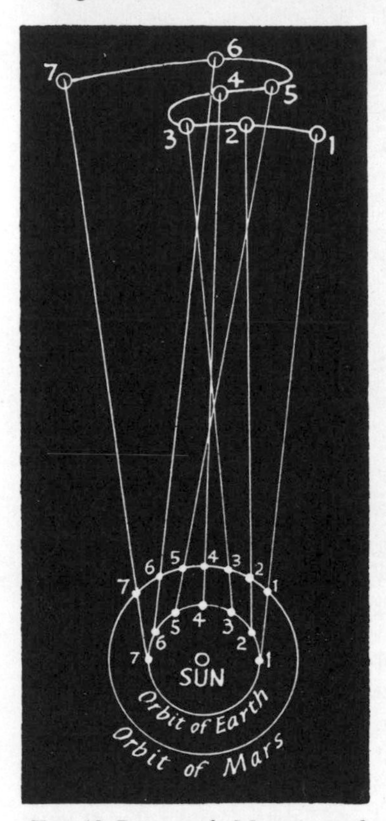

FIG. 10. Retrograde Movement of Mars

A further point of interest about the planetary orbits is that they all lie very much in the same plane, so that we are not far wrong when we draw them on a flat sheet of paper. This means that the planets can never wander near the celestial poles; they must keep relatively close to the *ecliptic*, which may be defined as the apparent yearly path of the Sun in the heavens. Of course, the coincidence is not exact – otherwise Mercury and Venus would appear in transit against the Sun at every inferior conjunction – but none of the planets, apart from Pluto and some of the asteroids, have orbits which are inclined to that of the Earth by as much as eight degrees.

A brief account of the planetary motions can give little indication of the enormous problems which confront the mathematical astronomer. Each planet pulls on its fellows, producing *perturbations* in their movements; the satellites of the major planets have also to be taken into account, and there are any number of uncertain quantities to be considered, such as the 'relativity' effect predicted by Einstein – which has turned out to be quite important in the case of Mercury, though it cannot possibly be properly explained in non-mathematical terms.

Astronomical handbooks publish orbits of the planets, but it should be remembered that these are only mean orbits—a planet does not follow exactly the same track in each journey round the Sun. An orbit depends primarily on the velocity of the planet, and of course this velocity is not constant. Taking every predictable perturbation into account, it is possible to compute an *osculating* orbit, which is much more accurate. For instance, the mean value for the eccentricity of the orbit of Neptune is known with high precision, but in early 1961 the planet was moving according to an orbit whose eccentricity was slightly less than the mean. Drawn on a diagram of conventional size, the difference between the two orbits would be concealed by the breadth of an inked line; but the actual difference between the hypothetical 'mean' position of Neptune at that time (calculated according to the mean orbit) and the real position of the planet (calculated according to the osculating orbit) amounted to 9,000,000 miles.[1]

This shows us how great are the complications with which astronomers have to deal. Yet on the whole, there is no doubt that they have succeeded wonderfully well in their attempts to unravel the problems of celestial mechanics. Uncertainties and errors are bound to remain, but our knowledge is much more complete than was the case not so very long ago.

[1] This was an example quoted by J. G. Porter at the March 1961 meeting of the British Astronomical Association. It was in fact Dr Porter's address which prompted me to write the paragraph given above.

Chapter 4

Planetary Probes

THERE ARE TWO WAYS of exploring the planets. One is by telescope; the other is by rocket. Most of this book will be concerned with pure astronomy, but in view of the startling development of the new science of astronautics it is wise to say at least something about artificial satellites, moon-rockets, and planetary probes.

The idea of reaching other worlds has always intrigued mankind. It is interesting to remember, for example, that as long ago as the second century A.D. a Greek writer named Lucian wrote a story about a voyage to the Moon. Lucian did not expect to be taken seriously; he was a satirist, and called his book the *True History* for the excellent reason that (in his own words) it was 'made up of nothing but lies from beginning to end'. It is an amusing tale, in which Lucian describes the remarkable adventures of a party of seamen whose ship was caught up in a waterspout and hurled on to the Moon.

Other stories followed in later years, but perhaps the first really important novel from a scientific point of view was written in 1865 by Jules Verne. It was called *From the Earth to the Moon*, and Verne made it as accurate as he could.

When we are considering space exploration, with either manned or unmanned vehicles, we can at once dispose of certain methods which cannot possibly be used either now or in the future. For instance, anyone who dreams of flying to the Moon by aeroplane is doomed to disappointment. Aircraft – both the 'old-fashioned' propeller machines and the modern jets – depend on the presence of a surrounding atmosphere. Without air, the propeller has nothing to grip and the jet has no oxygen supply to feed its motors. The Moon is a quarter of a million miles away, but the Earth's atmosphere stretches upward for only a few hundreds of miles above the ground, and so most of the journey has to be done in airless space. This means that all vehicles of the aeroplane type are useless astronautically.

Russian work has shown that traces of air may linger on to about 2,000 miles, but to all intents and purposes we can say that above 500 miles, at most, there is so little atmosphere left that we are entitled to disregard it. If we give a scale model in which the distance between the Earth and the Moon is reduced to 20 feet, our 500-mile atmospheric blanket is therefore represented by only half an inch.

Jules Verne's idea was to use a space-gun. His projectile, carrying three men as well as an assortment of animals, was to be placed in the barrel of a huge cannon and fired towards the Moon at a speed of 7 miles per second. Verne went to a great deal of trouble to make his calculations accurate, and he did indeed plan his book upon what he thought must be a sound scientific basis.

There was a special reason for starting the projectile off at 7 miles per second. The Earth has a strong gravitational pull, but any object given an initial velocity of 7 miles per second will escape from it; instead of falling back to the ground, it will leave the Earth permanently – which is why 7 miles per second is known as the Earth's *escape velocity*. The idea is easy enough to grasp by means of experimenting with a cricket ball, or for that matter any other solid body. The greater the starting velocity imparted to the ball, the higher it will rise before falling back. If it were possible for you to give the ball an initial speed of 7 miles per second, it would not fall back at all.

This is all very well – in theory; but there were several factors which Verne did not take into account, presumably because he did not know about them. The first is, simply, friction. Air exerts a considerable resistance, as anyone can prove by cupping a hand and swishing it downward. A solid body moving through the lower atmosphere at 7 miles per second would rub so violently against the air-particles that intense heat would be set up, and Verne's projectile would have been destroyed even before it had left the barrel of the gun. We have a practical demonstration of this effect every time we see a shooting-star, which is simply a small piece of matter dashing into the upper atmosphere and destroying itself.

Secondly, the shock of starting off at 7 miles per second would certainly prove fatal to any luckless occupant of the projectile. And thirdly, it must be added that even if a space-gun could send a vehicle to the Moon, the journey would be a one-way trip only, since there would be no means of return. Verne solved this problem very neatly in his story, but on the whole we must agree that space-guns belong to fiction and not to fact.

Having rejected aeroplanes and space-guns, we must think of something else. This brings us on to the rocket, which does not depend upon atmosphere at all, but functions in a completely different way.

A firework rocket of the kind used on November the Fifth consists of a tube filled with gunpowder, and with a hole or exhaust at one end. When you 'light the blue touch-paper and retire immediately', the gunpowder starts to burn, and gives off hot gas. This gas tries to get out of the rocket; it can do so only through the exhaust, and therefore rushes out of the exhaust in a concentrated stream. The effect is to propel the rocket body in the opposite direction. So long

FIG. 11. Principle of Reaction

as the gas continues to come out through the exhaust, the rocket will keep moving.

Again we can give an everyday analogy. Imagine a sleigh lying on smooth ice. If a boy stands on one end of it and then kicks off, the boy will move in one direction while the sleigh moves in the other. The boy is playing the part of the exhaust gases, while the sleigh represents the rocket tube. The experiment would work just as well in vacuum (assuming, of course, that the boy could breathe under such conditions!), and similarly a rocket can function in airless space. We come back to what Isaac Newton called the 'principle of reaction': every action has an equal and opposite reaction.

The main credit for suggesting that rockets might be used for interplanetary flight goes to a Russian, Konstantin Tsiolkovskii, who put forward the idea at the start of the present century. Tsiolkovskii also realized that solid fuels, such as gunpowder, are of limited use, since they are weak and uncontrollable. Instead, he planned to use liquid fuels, and in 1926 the first liquid-fuel rocket was successfully launched – not by Tsiolkovskii himself, who was purely a theorist, but by the American pioneer Robert Goddard.

Tremendous progress has been made since then. The war had something to do with it – many people will remember the V2 rockets launched by the Germans to bombard London – but rocketry would have been developed in any case, both for scientific use and military misuse. High-altitude vehicles have sent back information about the upper regions of the Earth's atmosphere, and have also been of great help to astronomers, since photographs taken from great heights can record all the radiations from space instead of only those which can penetrate the shielding layers in the lower air.

A modern launcher is a highly complex vehicle. It consists of several separate rockets mounted one on top of the other. As each motor uses up its fuel, part of the vehicle breaks away and falls back to the ground, while the upper parts continue their journey with increased speed as well as with full tanks. This 'step' principle is necessary because even the best modern fuels are of limited power, and rockets are very prodigal in using up their propellants. Once we learn enough to employ nuclear propellants we may be able to dispense with step-vehicles, but this lies in the future.

It is clear, too, that a rocket does not start off at full velocity. If it did, it would destroy itself by frictional heat. It can start at a slow speed, and work up to escape velocity only when it is beyond the denser part of the atmosphere. Once escape velocity has been reached, the power can be cut off, and the rocket will 'coast' for most of the journey.[1]

By the early 1950's the idea of space-research was no longer regarded as at all wild, and in 1955 the American authorities announced plans for sending up a small man-made moon or artificial satellite. The scheme involved taking an instrument-carrying vehicle up by means of a rocket, and putting it into an orbit round the Earth at a height of several hundreds of miles. Once suitably placed, and moving at the correct speed, it would not fall down; it would behave in precisely the same way as a natural astronomical body. Above 400

[1] If the rocket could go on using power for the whole flight, there would be no need to reach escape velocity at all; but here again the amount of propellant needed would be tremendous.

miles or so, such a satellite would be virtually unaffected by friction against the last traces of atmosphere.

At this point the centre of interest shifted abruptly from the United States to Soviet Russia. Apart from vague statements now and then, the Russians had given no indications of what they were planning, but on 1957 October 4 they suddenly launched Sputnik I, the first of the earth satellites. The scientific world was incredulous but admiring as the satellite sped round the globe, its radio transmitter sending out the famous 'Bleep! bleep!' signals which aroused so much comment.

Sputnik I moved in an elliptical path, and near perigee (its closest point to the Earth) it had to pass through appreciable atmosphere. Gradually the friction took its toll, and on January 4 of the following year the satellite came to the end of its career; it entered the denser air, and was destroyed in the same way as a shooting-star. However, it had done all that its makers had hoped.

Other earth satellites have since been launched from both America and Russia. One of the most spectacular was the U.S. Echo, which took the form of a plastic balloon coated with aluminium, and which shone like a bright, slowly moving star. At present (1962) there can be no doubt that the Russians lead the way, but Western scientists too are playing a major role – as the astronauts' flights have shown. The real tragedy is that the political situation does not allow free exchange of information.

Once earth satellites had been launched, a moon-rocket was the obvious next step. It was taken in 1959, when the Russians sent up their first three 'Lunik' vehicles. In January, Lunik I went past the Moon at a distance of only a few thousands of miles and then moved away into space, entering an orbit round the Sun and becoming a tiny artificial planet. Lunik II, launched in September, actually hit the Moon, and a month later Lunik III went round the Moon and sent back photographs which have proved of unique interest to astronomers.

The Moon is, of course, our nearest natural neighbour, and sending a rocket vehicle to any of the planets is much more difficult. Even with Mars or Venus the journey will last for months instead of less than two days, and problems of control are far greater. There is also the trouble of keeping radio contact. In February 1961, for instance, the Russians launched a probe vehicle towards Venus. It was expected to pass within 65,000 miles of Venus in mid-May, and it probably did so, but since all contact was lost after a few weeks we have no certain information.

Sending a vehicle from the Earth to another planet is not just a question of waiting until the planet is at its closest to us and then dispatching a rocket across the gap. Venus, at its nearest, is less than 25,000,000 miles away; but so long as we are limited to propellants of the sort now in use, the total distance covered by the rocket must be much greater than this. The vehicle is put into a *transfer orbit* which sends it in towards the Sun, until it reaches the orbit of Venus at the precise moment when Venus itself happens to be there. The same principles hold good for Mars, though in this case the vehicle must travel outwards. The slightest error in launching speed or direction will mean that the vehicle will miss its target not by a few miles, but by millions.

Planetary studies carried out by rocket probes are still at a very early stage, but there is no reason to doubt that they will be extended during the next few years, and great hopes are placed on them. Manned space-flight is a different matter altogether. We may assume that the first men will reach the Moon before many years are past, but when we consider a flight to Mars or Venus the associated 'minor' problems, such as food and air supply, turn out to be anything but minor.

Atomic power may solve many of our difficulties, but at the moment we do not know enough about the atom to make use of it in astronautics. We are still largely groping in the dark, and this is one reason why the military nuclear tests are so dangerous.[1] Obviously it is too early to speculate as to the form which atomic rockets may take, but they must be developed eventually, provided that we do not indulge in further warfare. In time to come, they may well supersede our present clumsy and inefficient chemical propellants.

Meanwhile, unmanned probes have arrived on the scene to join in the general programme of research. So let us now consider the members of the Sun's family one by one, and see where all this patient investigation by telescope and rocket is leading us.

[1] Statesmen tell us that the danger level of radioactivity in the atmosphere has not yet been reached. By the time it actually has been reached, they will hold a conference and decide to do something about it – blissfully oblivious to the fact that it will then be too late.

Chapter 5

Mercury

LONG AGO, SO LONG ago that we do not know just when, the ancient peoples noticed a bright star which could sometimes be seen in the western sky just after the Sun had set. It was not an ordinary star; it moved about, and so it could only be a planet. Later, it was identified with a similar planet seen from time to time in the eastern sky before sunrise. The Greeks named it in honour of the messenger of the gods, and certainly the little planet is always elusive and hard to catch. A famous but probably untrue story tells us that the great astronomer Copernicus died without ever having seen it.

In 1960 I tried to estimate how many times in each year Mercury could be seen with the naked eye. From my home in Sussex I was able to record it on seventeen different occasions. However, people who live in or near cities will be less favoured, since when Mercury is a naked-eye object it is always low down in the sky.

Mercury revolves round the Sun at an average distance of 36,000,000 miles, and is the closest-in of the planets. One known asteroid (Icarus) and a large number of comets have the temerity to approach closer to the solar surface, but no other important bodies move in these torrid regions. A century ago, however, an intra-Mercurian planet was believed to exist; its presence was regarded as well established, and it was even given a name – Vulcan. The story of this so-called 'discovery' is most interesting, and is a first-class example of how even the most brilliant scientists can be misled.

The Director of the Paris Observatory at that time was named Le Verrier. He was probably the greatest astronomer of his day, and had been personally responsible for adding a new planet to the known members of the Solar System. He had discovered that Uranus, then the most remote planet known, was not moving according to theory; something was pulling it out of its path, and Le Verrier's calculations led to the tracking-down of the disturbing planet, now named

Neptune.[1] In 1860, some fifteen years after this triumph, Le Verrier arrived at a similar result for Mercury; the 'messenger of the gods' was not where he should be, and it seemed reasonable to assume that this was due to the attraction of an intra-Mercurian planet.

This was not actually the case. Many years later Einstein's theory of relativity cleared up the discrepancy without involving an unknown planet at all. But at about the time that Le Verrier finished his calculations a French doctor named Lescarbault wrote to say that he had watched an intra-Mercurian planet passing in transit across the face of the Sun.

At some inferior conjunctions both Mercury and Venus do pass across the Sun, and presumably any inner planet would do the same – which, incidentally, would be almost the only hope of observing it at all. Le Verrier made haste to visit Lescarbault, and despite the doctor's rather strange methods (for instance, he recorded time by an old watch which lacked its second hand, and he recorded his observations with chalk upon wooden boards, planing them off when he had no further use for them), Le Verrier decided that a new planet had indeed come to light. He named it 'Vulcan', and worked out that it was 13,000,000 miles from the Sun, with a periodic time of 19¾ days and a diameter of something like a thousand miles. He also calculated the times of future transits.

Yet Vulcan has never since been seen, and it is now certain that what Lescarbault saw – if, indeed, he saw anything – was not a planet. It may have been a sunspot; but it is interesting to note that Liais, in Brazil, had been observing the Sun at the exact time of Vulcan's supposed transit and had seen nothing at all.

Interest was rekindled for a time in 1878, when there was a total eclipse of the Sun. At a total eclipse the Moon passes directly in front of the Sun and blots out the bright solar disk, so that stars can be seen for a few minutes in the middle of the day. Two American observers, Watson and Swift, carried out a careful search, and claimed that they had recorded various unidentified starlike objects. However, Watson's and Swift's observations agreed neither with the predicted Vulcan nor with each other, and little reliance can be placed upon them. It is now quite definite that Vulcan does not exist,

[1] J. C. Adams, in England, reached a similar result at about the same time. The full story of the discovery of Neptune will be told in Chapter 14.

and that Mercury is the first planet we encounter in our journey outward from the Sun.

Mercury is not at all easy to observe, partly because it always seems inconveniently close to the Sun in the sky, and partly because it is small and comparatively distant. According to the French

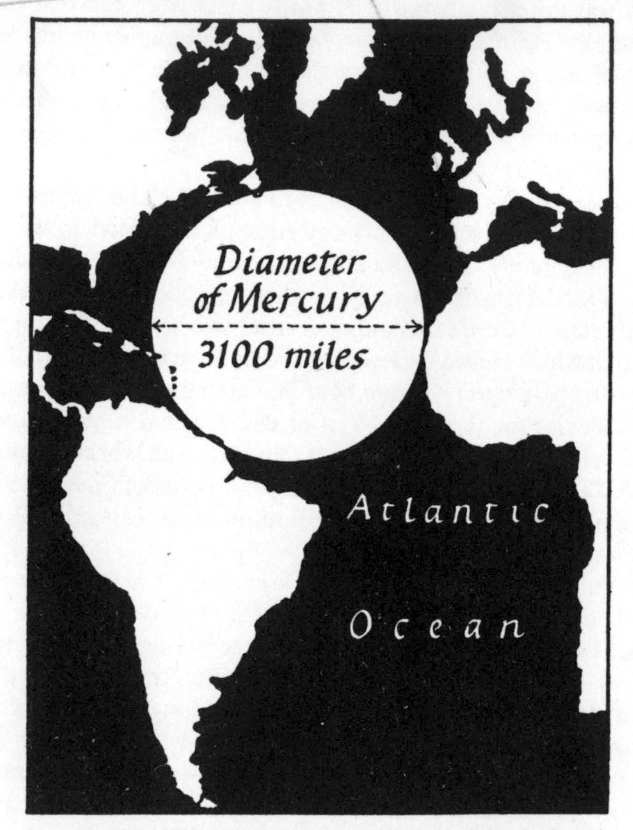

FIG. 12. Size of Mercury, compared with the Atlantic Ocean

astronomers H. Camichel and P. Muller, its diameter is 2,900 miles; in 1960, measures carried out by G. de Vaucouleurs gave 3,030 miles. Mercury is thus not a great deal larger than the Moon, though considerably more massive. There is the further difficulty that when it is at its closest to the Earth, at inferior conjunction, it cannot normally be seen at all, as its non-luminous night hemisphere is then turned towards us. All things considered, it is not surprising that our knowledge of the surface features of Mercury remains rather slight.

The first serious telescopic observations of Mercury were made towards the end of the eighteenth century. Sir William Herschel, discoverer of the planet Uranus and an observer of genius, could detect virtually no surface markings even with his powerful telescopes; more positive results were obtained by a German amateur, Johann Schröter, who constructed the first proper chart of the planet and believed, quite reasonably, that he had detected definite and permanent markings. Unfortunately Schröter, though an honest and painstaking observer, was not a good draughtsman, and some of his reported 'discoveries', such as that of a mountain eleven miles high, are rather hard to credit. It is unlikely that he could have succeeded where Herschel had failed.

It was left to a keen-eyed Italian astronomer, G. V. Schiaparelli, to draw up a comparatively reliable map of Mercury. Rather than wait for sunset, when the planet was of course low in the sky, Schiaparelli made most of his observations in broad daylight, and between 1881 and 1889 he plotted a number of dark, well-defined streaks and patches against the generally pinkish background. He also attacked the problem of Mercury's rotation period, i.e. the length of its 'day'.

Schröter had adopted a value of 24 hours, almost the same length as for the Earth, but Schiaparelli's work led him to the unexpected conclusion that Mercury keeps one hemisphere turned permanently towards the Sun, with the other plunged in perpetual night. This means that Mercury revolves once on its axis in exactly the same time that it takes to go once round the Sun – approximately 88 terrestrial days.

If Mercury had no axial spin at all, each part of its surface would see the Sun at some time or other, as can easily be shown by means of a simple experiment. Place a chair in the middle of a room to represent the Sun, and represent Mercury by your head. Now look at the chair and walk round it. If you want to keep your face turned towards the chair, you must turn slowly as you walk; otherwise the back of your head will be turned towards the chair after you have gone halfway round. By the time you have come back to your starting-point, you will have turned once; and this is how Schiaparelli considered that Mercury must behave.

Recent studies have shown that he was right, and that consequently the terms 'day' and 'night' have no real meaning so far as Mercury is concerned. One hemisphere is perpetually scorched by the solar rays, while no gleams of sunlight ever penetrate to the far side. Truly, the innermost planet is a curious world.

There is a perfectly logical reason for this strange state of affairs. In the early part of its existence as a separate body, Mercury may well have been hot and plastic,[1] with a relatively rapid spin. Just as the Moon raises tides in the oceans of the Earth, so the Sun raised tides in the viscous body of Mercury; material was heaped up in a bulge in the Sun's direction, and as Mercury spun on its axis the solar pull tended to keep the bulge stationary. The result was that Mercury's speed of rotation was steadily slowed down until, relative to the Sun, it had ceased altogether; the 'day' became equal to the 'year', and the tidal bulge remained permanently pointing to the Sun.

If Mercury revolved round the Sun at uniform speed, exactly half the planet would be permanently sunlit. Actually the situation is rather more complicated. Undoubtedly the planet spins on its axis at a constant speed, but its velocity in orbit changes. Mercury's orbit is more elliptical than that of the Earth, and the distance from the Sun varies between 28½ million miles at perihelion to 43½ million at aphelion. The smaller the distance, the greater the orbital speed, in conformity with the traffic laws of the Solar System; and whereas Mercury hastens along at some 36 miles a second when near perihelion, the speed drops to only 24 miles a second near aphelion. The axial rotation can, therefore, get 'out of step'. Sometimes, the rotation is a little ahead of itself with respect to the planet's position in orbit; sometimes a little behind.

Consequently, the Sun must seem to sway in the Mercurian sky, and there is a fairly wide belt – between the region of permanent day and the region of everlasting night – where the Sun will rise and set. Astronomers have nicknamed this region the 'Twilight Zone'. Its exact limits are uncertain, since we have no definite information about the planet's axial inclination.

Mercury never comes much within 50 million miles of the Earth, and it is not surprising that its surface details are invisible with small telescopes. The most reliable surface chart was drawn up over

[1] Different astronomers have different views about this; but as we have seen, there is no general agreement as to how the planets were formed.

a quarter of a century ago by E. M. Antoniadi, a Greek astronomer who spent much of his life in France and did his observational work with the 33-inch refractor of the Observatory of Meudon. Like

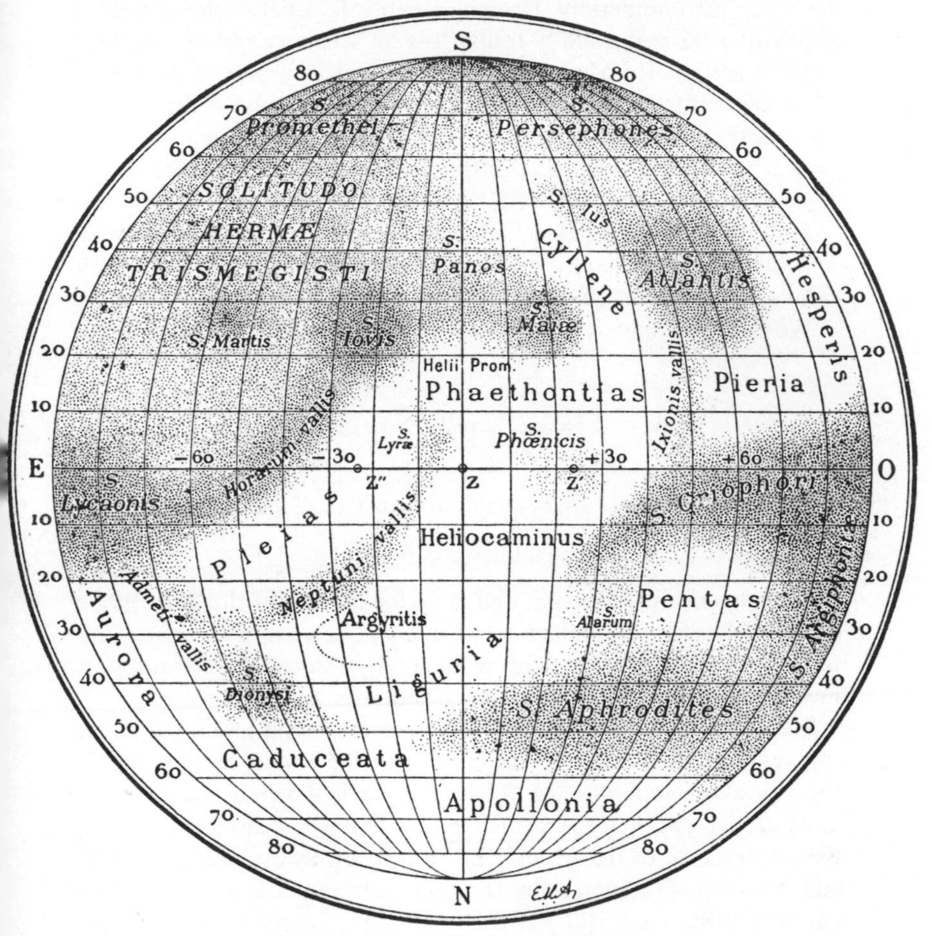

FIG. 13. Antoniadi's chart of Mercury
(Reproduced by kind permission of MM. Gauthier-Villars Press, Paris)

Schiaparelli, he made his observations when the Sun was above the horizon and Mercury high in the sky, but he had a great advantage telescopically, since the Meudon refractor is one of the finest in the world.

Antoniadi's chart agreed reasonably well with Schiaparelli's, and he also gave names to the light and dark areas which have now passed into general use. He died during the war, but his work was continued by other astronomers in France, notably B. Lyot – whose sudden death in 1952 was such a tragic loss to science – and A. Dollfus. Dollfus has studied Mercury with the 24-inch refractor of the Pic du Midi Observatory, situated high in the Pyrenees above the densest and most troublesome layers of the Earth's atmosphere, and has produced important work. Dollfus must, indeed, be regarded as the leading modern authority with regard to Mercury.

However, we must admit that even the maps drawn by Antoniadi and Dollfus are probably no more than approximate, and the positions of the more delicate features may well be subject to large errors.

We can never have a proper view of 'full Mercury', as the planet is

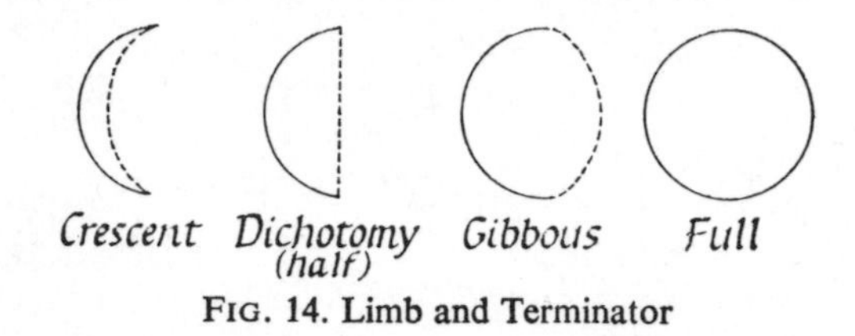

FIG. 14. Limb and Terminator

then at superior conjunction and is on the far side of the Sun. When at its brightest to the naked eye, Mercury shows as a crescent. The phases are quite obvious with a moderate-sized telescope, and it is interesting to follow the changing position of the *terminator*.

The terminator is the boundary between the sunlit and night hemispheres, and should not be confused with the *limb*, which is merely the edge of the apparent disk. The difference is shown in the diagram, in which the terminator is dotted and the limb shown as a continuous line. In the case of the Moon, the terminator always appears rough and broken, with mountain summits catching the sunlight while adjacent valleys are still bathed in shadow. Mercury is so far off that its terminator appears virtually smooth, but occasional projections and irregularities have been reported, which lends support to the theory that the surface is mountainous in character. The horns of the crescent are known as the *cusps*. As long ago as 1800 Schröter noted that the upper or southern[1] cusp is usually blunter than the

[1] Since all common astronomical telescopes give an inverted picture, drawings are conventionally made with south at the top and north at the bottom.

northern, and reference to the charts will show why. The southern part of the disk is darker than the northern, and includes the large grey area which Antoniadi named the Solitudo Hermæ Trismegisti – the 'Wilderness of Hermes the Thrice Greatest'.

The Mercurian markings are certainly permanent, and are thus features of the actual surface of the planet. Their precise nature is not known, since we cannot see them clearly enough to come to any decision, but the grey areas may be similar to the waterless 'seas' of the Moon. It will be important to find out whether Mercury is scarred with lunar-type craters, but space-research developments give us our only real hope of finding out.

For many years it was uncertain whether or not Mercury possessed any sort of atmospheric mantle. At least it seemed safe to assume that a dense atmosphere did not exist, because Mercury has a relatively feeble pull, and would be unable to hold down an atmosphere of such a kind. The whole matter depends on the value of the escape velocity, which in the case of Mercury is only 2¼ miles per second.

The Earth, as we have seen, has an escape velocity of 7 miles per second. The particles making up the bulk of our atmosphere cannot move so quickly as this, and so cannot leak away into space; but things are very different on the Moon, where the critical velocity is only 1½ miles per second. In its early existence the Moon may well have had an appreciable atmosphere, but the lunar gravity was unable to hold the atmosphere down, so that today the Moon is virtually 'airless'. Mercury is a borderline case. It should be able to retain heavy gases, in which the particles move comparatively slowly, but a terrestrial-type atmosphere is certainly out of the question.

Direct studies can be made when Mercury passes in transit across the face of the Sun. On these occasions the planet appears as a small, sharply defined dark spot, with no trace of blurring round the edges. A dense atmospheric layer round Mercury would cause a 'fuzzy' appearance, as is actually the case for Venus.

Mercury's orbit is inclined to ours at an angle of seven degrees, and transits are therefore infrequent. The last took place on 1960 November 7; the next few will occur on 1970 May 9, 1973 November 10, 1986 November 13, and 1993 November 6. (Transits can occur only in May or November.) Strange appearances have been reported now and then during past transits, but it seems that all these must be put down to defects in eyes or instruments. When in

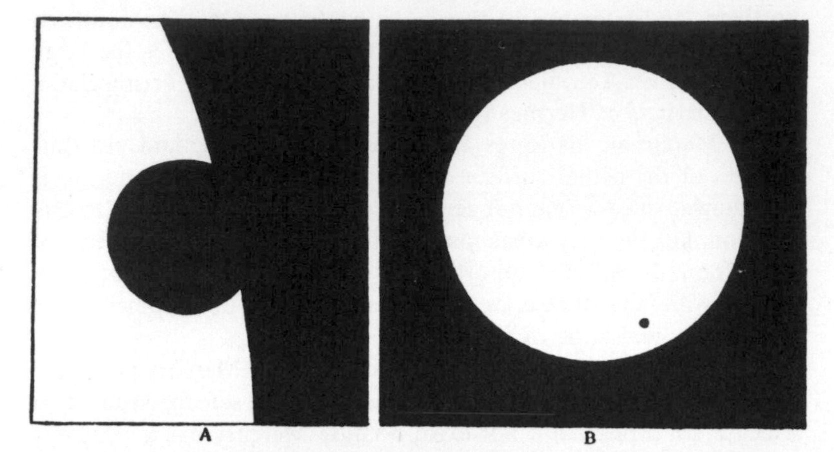

FIG. 15. Transits of Mercury: A 1914 Nov. 6; B 1953 Nov. 14
(3-inch O.G., direct vision; H. P. Wilkins)

transit, Mercury is too inconspicuous to be seen with the naked eye, but a small telescope will show it clearly.[1]

Yet both Schiaparelli and Antoniadi claimed that the dark areas of Mercury were often veiled by whitish clouds, and Antoniadi even stated that these clouds were 'more frequent and obliterating than those of Mars'. Needless to say, there was never any suggestion that the clouds were similar to those of the Earth; water-droplets on the day side of Mercury would be as short-lived as snowflakes in a blast-furnace. Until fairly recently, the existence of clouds of some sort was regarded as established; but observations made at the Pic du Midi led Dollfus, in 1953, to state that he 'had never seen a modification of the aspect of the surface definitely attributable to atmospheric clouds', so that the whole question seems to be open once more.

Dollfus has, however, reported the presence of a tenuous atmosphere. It is thin, with a ground density of not more than $\frac{3}{1000}$ of that of the Earth's atmosphere at sea-level, and corresponds to what we normally describe as a laboratory vacuum; a barometer would record a pressure of only about one millimetre, which is negligible. We can

[1] It must be remembered that the Sun should never be viewed directly through a telescope, even with the protection of a dark cap over the object-glass. The only sensible way to carry out solar observation is by projection of the Sun's image, which gives better results and involves no danger to the eye. During transits, Mercury may be well seen in this way.

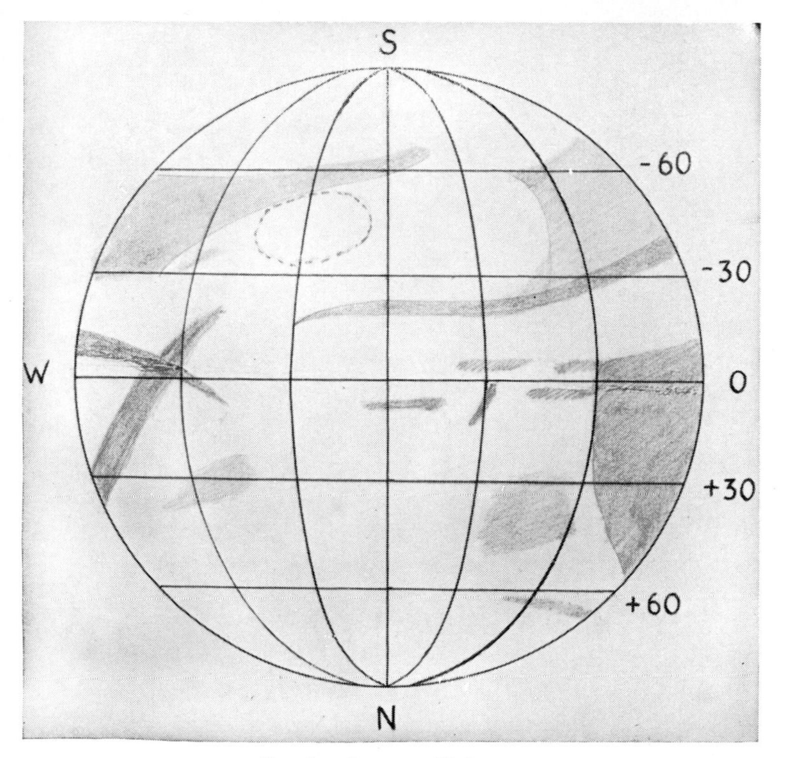

I Sandner's map of Mercury

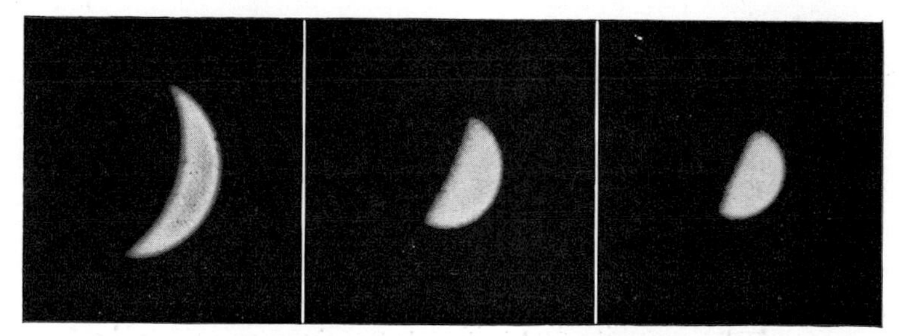

II Photographs of Venus (E. A. Whitaker, Greenwich Observatory)
(*Reproduced by kind permission of the Astronomer Royal*)

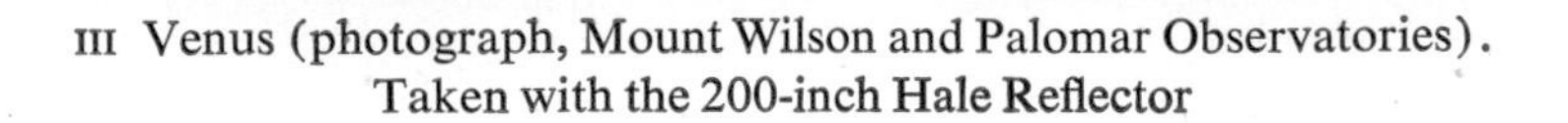

III Venus (photograph, Mount Wilson and Palomar Observatories). Taken with the 200-inch Hale Reflector

only guess at its composition, but the heavy gas carbon dioxide seems to be one possibility.

Dollfus' methods were necessarily indirect, and the observations are very delicate. In 1961 the Russian astronomer N. Kozirev, in the Crimea, decided to check them by taking advantage of a total eclipse of the Sun.

A solar eclipse occurs when the Moon passes in front of the Sun and blots out the bright disk, so that the Sun's surroundings – the chromosphere and corona – flash into view. The sight is magnificent, and is of great importance to solar physicists. The track of totality at the eclipse of 1961 February 15 passed across Europe, from south France through north Italy, Jugoslavia and the Crimean peninsula, covering three major observatories – St Michel (France), Arcetri (Italy), and the Crimean Astrophysical Observatory (U.S.S.R.).

Normally, Mercury is visible against a dark sky only when it is low down, so that it cannot be properly studied. During a total eclipse, however, the glare of the Sun is removed, and for a brief period Mercury may be seen against a dark background when it is high up. Kozirev spent the two and a half minutes of totality in using special instruments to see whether he could record any trace of atmosphere round Mercury,[1] but with negative results. It is a pity that opportunities of this kind are so infrequent; the next total eclipse visible from Britain will not take place until 1999.

Even a thin mantle might be capable of supporting dust, and if Antoniadi's clouds really exist they are presumably made up of dusty material. However, it is not easy to see just how they could spring up. Winds in so tenuous an atmosphere would be unable to cause violent dust-storms, and neither are volcanic eruptions to be expected upon a world so dormant as Mercury. On the whole, it now seems that the existence of 'clouds' in any form is unlikely.

Mercury is so small and remote that its surface temperature is difficult to measure with any accuracy. Measures made by Pettit and Nicolson at the Mount Wilson Observatory, in California, indicate that in the day-zone the temperature may rise to over 700 degrees

[1] It must require great mental resolution to remain in the track of a total eclipse and yet not look at the Sun at all; but this is what astronomers often have to do. Conditions in 1961 were generally good, though from Britain, where the eclipse was partial, the weather was cloudy. An interesting sidelight was that for the first time the eclipse was shown on television, and I have vivid memories of carrying through the B.B.C. commentary from my site on the top of a lonely mountain in Jugoslavia!

Fahrenheit, and this is certainly of the right order. In sharp contrast, the night-zone is bitterly cold. The atmosphere is quite incapable of carrying any heat round to the regions where no solar rays penetrate, and in consequence the temperature there cannot be very far above absolute zero. Remote Pluto, the outermost member of the Sun's family, spins on its axis in a much shorter time than it takes to go once round the Sun, so that every part of its surface is periodically illuminated; this alone must raise the temperature above that of the sun-starved hemisphere of Mercury. It is therefore incorrect to say simply that Mercury is the hottest of the planets. It is also the coldest.

There is no reason to doubt that instrumented probe rockets will be sent to Mercury in the foreseeable future, but whether men will ever land there is much more doubtful. Even when Mars and Venus have been reached, which should be within the next century or two, Mercury may well remain unexplored. Yet there can be no harm in controlled speculation – so long as we remember that it *is* speculation – so what would we see if it were possible for us to land in the 'twilight zone', between the zone of everlasting day and the zone of everlasting night?

High, cracked mountains casting immense shadows across the barren surface; a vast, glaring sun low down near the horizon; an eternal desert which has never known life. All is silent; sound-waves are carried by atmosphere, and the thin mantle of Mercury is too tenuous to carry even the whisper of a sound. A dazzling planet high in the sky, cloud-covered Venus; a second planet attended by a starlike companion – the Earth and its Moon. But we would not linger for long. Mercury is a dead world, as alien and unfriendly as it can possibly be.

Chapter 6

Venus

IT IS QUITE REFRESHING to turn from the dead, inhospitable Mercury to Venus, the second planet from the Sun, which could hardly present a greater contrast. It moves in much the same manner as Mercury, showing phases, and appearing sometimes as a morning, and sometimes as an evening star; but there the resemblance ends.

Originally the morning and evening stars were thought to be different bodies, and they were even given different names, Phosphorus and Hesperus; but as long ago as 500 B.C. Pythagoras, the great Greek geometer, realized that the two are identical. Venus is in fact so brilliant that it must have been known even at the dawn of history, and it far outshines every other celestial body apart from the Sun and Moon.

Venus is considerably closer to the Sun than we are. Its average distance is 67,000,000 miles, and this does not vary much, since the orbit is nearly circular. At inferior conjunction, Venus can approach to within 25,000,000 miles of the Earth, and is therefore our nearest neighbour in the Solar System except for the Moon and an occasional comet or asteroid. The periodic time is 224¾ days, and therefore an Earth boy of fifteen would be twenty-four 'years' old according to the Cytherean[1] calendar. The orbital speed, 21¾ miles per second, is correspondingly greater than ours.

Mercury is shy and elusive in the twilight, but there is nothing shy about Venus, which is easily visible in broad daylight under favourable conditions. This great brilliance is partly due to the fact that Venus is an excellent reflector of sunlight, and partly because it is a comparatively large world. Its diameter is almost the same as that of the Earth – 7,700 miles as against 7,927 – and the mass and

[1] There is no universally accepted adjective for Venus. 'Venusian' and 'Venerian' have their supporters, but both terms are ugly. 'Cytherean', derived from one of the names of the mythological Goddess of Love, is perhaps preferable, even though some Classical scholars may object to it.

escape velocity are also similar, so that an Earthman who lands on Venus will feel about the same weight as he does at home.

Unfortunately we cannot see Venus at all when it is at its closest. This is the time of inferior conjunction, when the 'night' side is turned towards us, and in any case the planet is very near the Sun in the sky. Venus appears brightest when at the crescent stage, with about 30 per cent. of the daylight hemisphere turned towards us; this is because the planet is then closer than when more fully illuminated. The 'full Venus', approaching superior conjunction, shows a much smaller apparent diameter, and at the actual point of superior conjunction Venus is on the far side of the Sun – at a distance of some 160,000,000 miles.

FIG. 16. Apparent Diameter of Venus

When at its best, Venus may set as much as $5\frac{1}{2}$ hours after the Sun; it can then be seen against a dark background, and looks like a small, glittering lamp in the sky. It can even cast shadows. I have a personal recollection of this. It was on a Sussex beach late one evening; Venus was dazzlingly bright, and I could see my shadow thrown beside me on to the sand.

Venus is so magnificent to the naked eye that it comes as a surprise to find that it is a great disappointment telescopically. In place of the mountains, valleys, oceans and plains which we might reasonably expect to see, all we can make out is a bright, almost blank disk. The explanation is obvious enough; we are not seeing the actual surface of Venus at all, but merely the upper layers of a deep, 'cloudy' atmosphere. We can never see beneath the 'clouds', and they hide the surface permanently, so that we can do little more than guess at the conditions on Venus itself.

However, any small telescope will show the phase, and the fact that Venus behaves in this way has been known ever since Galileo first turned his 'optick tube' to the planet in 1610. There are even a few well-authenticated cases of people who have been able to see the crescent form without any optical aid whatever; good binoculars will show the phases quite well.

The time when Venus becomes a perfect half is known as *dichotomy*. The movements of the planet are known with great accuracy, and dichotomy can thus be predicted, but strangely enough the predicted time is generally wrong. When Venus is approaching inferior conjunction, and is therefore waning, dichotomy occurs early; when Venus is waxing, dichotomy is late. Discrepancies of a fortnight or more have been reported, but it seems that these are subject to observational error, and that the true difference between actual and theoretical dichotomy is unlikely to exceed four days at most. I was able to carry out some careful studies in 1959, and found that before inferior conjunction dichotomy was two days early; after inferior conjunction, dichotomy was late by approximately the same amount.

Observations of this kind are not new. Schröter first noticed the discrepancies a hundred and fifty years ago, and explained them (not very convincingly) by the falling-off of light near the terminator. Shadows cast by tall mountains across Venus' surface have also been suggested. However, it is much more likely that the effect is purely optical. The planet's atmosphere may be concerned in some way, but preliminary measures indicate that the almost 'airless' Mercury behaves in the same fashion.

When Venus is near inferior conjunction, and therefore relatively close to us, it appears as a large, slender crescent, and from time to time roughnesses and irregularities have been reported in the terminator. We know that the terminator of the Moon is always broken and jagged, because the lunar surface is mountainous; similar appearances in the terminator of Venus might lead us to believe that there are mountains there too.

On three occasions between 1789 and 1793, Schröter described a bright, starlike point clear of the terminator of the crescent Venus, and attributed it to a peak. He measured it carefully, and calculated that it rose to a height of no less than 27½ miles above the surface! As Venus is almost the Earth's twin in size and mass, and our own mountains rise to less than six miles above sea-level, a gigantic peak of this sort does not appear likely; but there is no need to assume anything of the sort, even if we accept the accuracy of Schröter's observation (which many authorities do not). A high 'cloud' could equally well have been responsible.

Most serious observers of Venus have noted terminator dents and projections, but it does not seem probable that mountains are the cause. We know that the disk is not of uniform brilliancy; dusky areas are seen, and also brighter patches. A dusky part of the terminator, hemmed in by two brighter areas, would appear as an indentation, whereas a brilliant patch between two darker ones would appear to project. Observations carried out between 1950 and 1961 have led me to the conclusion that all the irregularities can be explained in this way. The surface of Venus may well be mountainous, but so far we have not the slightest proof.

More interesting are the bright caps at the horns or cusps of Venus, which can become quite striking, and are certainly worth describing.

The cusps often appear brighter than the rest of the planet, but at times brilliant, well-defined caps appear, sometimes a little way from the actual cusp and sometimes covering the cusp itself. They are not always visible, but when at their best are too conspicuous to be overlooked.

The polar caps of Mars are well known, and are certainly due to some icy or frosty deposit. Seen from space, the Earth also would show polar caps. It is tempting to suggest that the bright areas on Venus are due to the same cause, but a moment's thought shows us that there are any number of difficulties in the way of accepting ice or snow there.

For one thing, we know that the planet's atmosphere is deep enough and 'cloudy' enough to mask the surface completely, and it would therefore be impossible for us to see icefields even if they existed. The idea of elevated polar plateaux is decidedly far-fetched, and in any case recent measures confirm the old belief that the surface temperature is high. Altogether the snow theory seems to be quite unacceptable, and we must look elsewhere for an explanation of the cusp-caps.

It must also be remembered that we do not even know whether the caps mark the poles of Venus at all. We have no certain information about the tilt of the axis. Photographic studies by G. P. Kuiper lead him to the conclusion that the equator is inclined to the orbital plane by 32 degrees, as against 23½ degrees for the Earth, but although this seems plausible enough there is no proof that it is even approximately correct.

Some authorities consider that the cusp-caps are not real, but are due purely to contrast effects. Contrast may admittedly play a part, but on the whole it seems more likely that the caps are genuine phenomena. They are not always visible; sometimes one cap may be seen while the other is absent, and often enough there is no trace of either. If they were due to contrast, they might be expected to remain constant under similar conditions of phase.

During recent years there have been attempts to find out whether there is any periodicity in the behaviour of the caps. So far the results are tentative, but there are signs of a period of four or five weeks. If so, it may well be that the caps are truly polar, and are atmospheric phenomena caused by some feature of the air-circulation in the polar regions of Venus, while the rotation period may also amount to four or five weeks.

The disk itself shows only vague features, so hazy that their positions cannot be defined with any real accuracy; indeed it is probably true to say that Venus is one of the most difficult of all celestial bodies to observe – instead of being the easiest, as we would have every right to expect from its size and nearness. Frequently no details whatsoever can be made out, and Venus shows nothing but its characteristic phase.

Yet dusky shadings may be seen from time to time, and may be observed with a relatively small telescope. They are hazy and delicate, and far too nebulous to draw with any accuracy – but they are definitely there.

Early telescopic observers recorded hard and sharp features, and the Italian astronomer F. Bianchini went so far as to draw up a map based on work carried out between 1727 and 1732. He showed oceans, continents, promontories and straits, and certainly believed that the features were permanent. Actually the small, long-focus refractor which he used was quite inadequate to show anything of the sort, and it is not likely that any of the features which he recorded were genuine. His chart is interesting historically, but it has no scientific value.

In the present century another attempt at map-making was carried out by Percival Lowell, the American astronomer who is best remembered for his work on Mars. Lowell believed Mars to be covered with a network of narrow, straight canals, the work of intelligent beings; and he constructed an observatory at Flagstaff, under the clear skies of Arizona, specially to observe the planets. His main telescope was a 24-inch refractor, and between 1892 and his death, in 1916, he made thousands of drawings of both Mars and Venus.

His sketches of Venus are remarkable, to say the least of it. Instead of soft nebulous shadings, he recorded hard, sharp, linear features, and described them as follows:

> The markings are long and narrow, but unlike the finer markings on Mars, have the appearance of being natural and not artificial . . . The markings, which are a straw-coloured grey, bear the look of ground or rock, and it is presumable from this that we see simply barren rock or sand weathered by æons of exposure to the Sun. I have seen the markings when their contours had the look of a steel engraving.

Lowell thus rejected the whole idea of a dense, all-concealing Cytherean atmosphere, and reverted to the old theory of a visible surface. Yet his linear markings have never since been seen by any observer equipped with a telescope of comparable size, and it seems safe to say that they do not exist in the form in which he drew them.

It often happens that a small telescope will show what looks at first sight rather like a streak, and in planetary work the question of aperture is all-important. There are two schools of thought. It has been said that 'the larger the telescope, the less one sees on Venus', the reason given being the fact that although a high magnification increases the apparent size of the disk, it also increases the blurring due to the Earth's unsteady atmosphere. I disagree strongly with this view, and have carried out some practical experiments in connection with it. My own observations of Venus have been carried out mainly with a 12½-inch reflector, but I have also made many drawings with smaller apertures (6 inches and even 3 inches) as well as with giant telescopes such as the Meudon 33-inch refractor. Generally, I have found that under good conditions the true features, such as the shadings and the cusp-caps, are always better seen with the larger instruments. On one occasion in 1961 I made drawings of Venus successively with a 6-inch reflector, a 12½-inch reflector, and a 24-inch reflector. With the 6-inch, nothing definite could be seen; two nebulous shadings and a cusp-cap were just detectable with the 12½-inch, and were easily visible with the 24-inch.

Apart from Lowell, who, incidentally, recorded sharp lines not only upon Venus and Mars but also upon various other bodies (such as Mercury and the four large satellites of Jupiter), the only observers to draw sharp linear markings on Venus are those equipped with inadequate telescopes. This indicates that the lines are due to tricks of the eye. A certain streakiness may be seen at times, but certainly nothing in the way of a 'canal', and it does not seem likely that there are any permanently visible features on Venus.[1]

Photography is of limited value in this connection, and in fact most photographs of Venus show no details at all. The best results have been obtained by taking photographs in light of short wavelength. In this way definite markings have been recorded, first by F. E. Ross at Mount Wilson and more recently by G. P. Kuiper and others. These, too, must be atmospheric in nature. Light of short wavelength has little penetrating power, and so presumably the markings are due to high-altitude 'clouds'.

One of the outstanding problems of Venus concerns the length of its rotation period or 'day'. If there were permanent surface markings, of course, a solution would be easy, since we could watch the markings being carried across the disk and so measure the period taken for the planet to make one complete turn. This has actually been done for Mars, and the time of rotation is known to within a fraction of a second. But the shadings on Venus are much too hazy and short-lived to be of much use, and though many estimates have been made we are still very much in the dark.

Early observers attacked the problem energetically, and announced various periods of around 24 hours. Further estimates followed in the nineteenth century. Leo Brenner, in 1896, gave a period accurate to within a thousandth of a second – which is rather like measuring the age of the Earth to the nearest minute! It must be admitted that visual studies of this sort simply cannot give a reliable answer,

[1] A. Dollfus and other French observers have published charts which are said to show some more or less permanent features; but while I have the greatest respect for these observers, I am bound to differ from them in this instance, since I believe that all features on Venus are impermanent.

because no recorded shading has been definite enough or long-enduring enough to have its drift measured. In any case, the local wind-systems would have to be taken into account, and about these we know nothing at all. I have been making regular drawings of Venus ever since 1934, but apart from the suspected periodicity of the cusp-caps I have found them of no help in the rotation period problem.

Some time ago I made a list of all the published rotation periods covering the years from 1666 to 1961. There were eighty-five of them, ranging from 22 hours 17 minutes (J. D. Kraus, 1956), to 224·7 days (originally suggested by G. V. Schiaparelli in 1890). There is no general agreement whatsoever, and it seems that we may disregard all those estimates which are based on visual work alone. Photography is slightly more helpful, and G. P. Kuiper has used photographic studies in drawing up his estimate of 'a few weeks' – possibly about one month. Yet the whole question is still completely open.

Schiaparelli believed that Venus, like Mercury, has a 'captured' rotation – that is to say the axial rotation period is equal to the 'year' of 224·7 days, in which case Venus would keep the same hemisphere turned permanently towards the Sun. Lowell, from a study of his so-called steel engravings, came to the same conclusion, and it has been supported in more recent years by A. Dollfus and other French astronomers. Yet it rests on very uncertain evidence, at best, and it is not supported by temperature measurements. So far as we can tell, the bright side of Venus is at about the same temperature as the dark side, which would not be the case if the rotation were of the same type as Mercury's.

The amount of heat sent to us by Venus is, of course, very small, but even so it can be measured by a special instrument known as a thermocouple. If we take two wires made of different metals, and solder their ends together to make a complete circuit, an electric current will be set up if the joins are at different temperatures. A current can, therefore, be produced by warming one of the joins and keeping the other at a constant temperature; and even the tiny current produced by Venus can be measured.

E. Pettit and S. B. Nicolson, at Mount Wilson, used the great 100-inch reflecting telescope there to concentrate the radiation from Venus, and then measured the tiny current produced. After additional corrections had been made, they were able to give reliable values for the surface temperatures – or, more accurately, for the temperatures of the upper 'clouds'. They showed that the temperature of the day side was well below freezing point, but that the dark side was no colder. In 1956 W. M. Sinton and J. Strong, in America, made further measures which led to the same result. There is nothing surprising in the discovery that the top of the cloud-layer is cold, but the experiments seem fatal to the idea that one side of Venus never receives any direct sunlight.

But if there is evidence against a very long rotation period, there are also arguments against a period of around 24 hours. This time we make use not of the thermocouple, but of the spectroscope.

The spectroscope is perhaps the most powerful tool used by modern astronomers. It analyzes light, and splits it up into its component parts, so that we can find out what materials are present in the light-source. Moreover, we can detect the notion of a luminous body. If the body is approaching, its light will be slightly more blue than expected; if it is receding, the light will be slightly reddened. The actual change of colour is too small to be noticed, but the towards- or away-movement is detectable spectroscopically provided that the speed is fast enough.

If Venus is spinning rapidly, one limb must be approaching us and the other receding (unless the planet has a large axial inclination, which on the whole does not seem very probable). No spectroscopic effects of this sort have been found, despite careful studies, and it is generally agreed that the rotation must be relatively slow.

Yet another method was used by J. D. Kraus, at Ohio, in 1956. Celestial bodies send out radiations of all kinds – not only visible light, but also 'radio waves', which are of longer wavelength and are collected by special instruments known as radio telescopes. Kraus announced that he had detected such radiations from Venus, and suggested that they might be due to thunderstorms in the planet's atmosphere. They seemed to have definite periodicity, and from this he derived a rotation period of 22 hours 17 minutes. Unfortunately this does not agree with the spectroscopic results, and in any case the radio waves from Venus have not been detected anywhere except at Ohio. Most authorities are now inclined to believe that there has been an error in interpretation, and that these particular radio waves do not in fact emanate from Venus.

To sum up: the rotation period of Venus is still unknown. It is not likely that it is as long as the periodic time of 224·7 days, and it is not likely to be as short as 24 hours, but that is about as far as we can go. A recent result by V. Kotelnikov and I. Shklovsky, of the U.S.S.R., gives a value of 10 days, but on the whole the most probable value is about a month, and further researches – perhaps with rocket probes – are needed before we can come to any positive conclusions.

It is evident that all our efforts to probe the mysteries of Venus are checkmated by the hazy atmosphere which forms a mantle that we are unable to pierce. What, then, can we find out about the atmosphere itself?

Its existence has been known for a long time, since it was discovered in 1761 by M. V. Lomonosov, the first of Russia's great astronomers. The occasion was one of the rare transits of Venus across the face of the Sun. The appearance of the planet's limb led Lomonosov to infer, quite correctly, that there must be an atmosphere of considerable depth and density.

Transits of Venus are interesting to watch, because the black, slowly moving disk can be seen with the unaided eye. Unfortunately, no transits take place during the present century. The last two occurred in 1874 and 1882; the next will be in 2004 and 2012.

During the seventeenth century Edmond Halley, the second Astronomer Royal – best remembered in connection with his work on the periodical comet which is now named in his honour – improved on an earlier suggestion by James Gregory that transits of Venus might be used to measure the distance of the Sun. It was necessary to measure the exact time that the planet passed on to the solar face, and to make observations from widely scattered points on the Earth. As the whole method is now completely obsolete there is no point in describing it in detail, but in any case the accuracy was ruined by an effect known as the Black Drop. It was found that when Venus passes on to the Sun it seems to draw a strip of blackness after it; when this strip disappears, the transit has already begun. The effect is, of course, due to Venus' atmosphere. The 1874 and 1882 transits were well observed, but the results were most disappointing, and since there are now much better ways of working out the Sun's

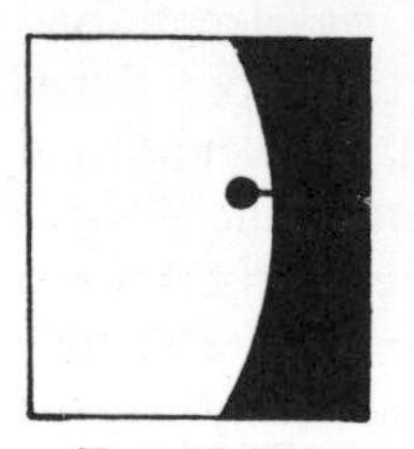

FIG. 17. The 'Black Drop'

distance the next pair of transits will not be regarded as of much importance.

No reference to transits would be complete without saying something about the incredible misfortunes suffered by a French astronomer, G. Legentil, in 1761 and 1769. The first of these transits was expected to be well seen from India, and accordingly Legentil set sail for Pondicherry. Unluckily for him the Seven Years' War was raging, and he did not arrive until after the transit was over. Rather than risk a second delay, he decided to remain where he was for the next eight years, and observe the 1769 transit instead. Fate could hardly have been more unkind. Shortly before and after the vital hours the sky was brilliantly clear; but the transit itself was completely hidden by clouds, and as it was rather too long for Legentil to wait until the next transit (that of 1874) he packed up what belongings he could and set off for home. Twice he was shipwrecked, and eventually reached Paris to learn that he had been presumed dead, so that his heirs were preparing to divide his property. Actually he lived for another twenty years, and did not die until 1792.

There is every reason to suppose that the depth of Venus' atmosphere is much the same as that of the Earth, and this has been confirmed by observations made when Venus itself passes in front of, and *occults*, a star. For a few seconds the star is seen shining through the planet's atmosphere, after which it is hidden by the solid body of Venus. Since the apparent rate of Venus' motion is known, the depth of the obscuring atmosphere can be worked out by measurements of how long the fading of the star lasts. In 1959 Venus occulted the bright star Regulus, in the constellation of the Lion, and various measures were made, all leading to much the same conclusion. I had an excellent view of this occultation, and was glad to do so, since it will be centuries before Venus again passes in front of a brilliant star.

Another atmospheric phenomenon which intrigued the early observers is the Ashen Light, or faint luminosity of the so-called 'dark' side of Venus against the brilliant crescent. It has been seen so often and by so many observers that its existence cannot be doubted, though its origin remains uncertain.

Something similar is seen in the case of the Moon, and is popularly known as 'the Old Moon in the Young Moon's arms'. It was correctly explained by Leonardo da Vinci as being due to light reflected from the Earth on to the Moon. Full moonlight can be brilliant, as we know well; to an observer on the lunar surface the Earth would appear as a glorious, shining globe, flooding the rocks with powerful radiance. However, no such explanation can account for the Ashen Light of moonless Venus, and some sort of atmospheric effect must be responsible.

The fact that the atmosphere is of considerable depth means that the cusps can appear prolonged in narrow lines of light, and the bright line may indeed be sometimes followed right round the dark hemisphere, forming a ring. But actual luminosity of the night side is another matter. Schröter was familiar with it, and Franz Gruithuisen, a well-known German astronomer of the mid-nineteenth century, believed it to be due to the glow from vast forest fires lighted by the inhabitants of Venus to celebrate the accession of a new ruler! There are, perhaps, some objections to Gruithuisen's theory, and a saner suggestion is that the Light is caused by strong auroræ in Venus' upper atmosphere.

Terrestrial auroræ, or Polar Lights, are high-level atmospheric glows produced by streams of electrified particles sent out by the Sun. There is no reason why similar effects should not occur on Venus, and they may in fact be stronger, since the distance from the Sun is less. Very possibly the Ashen Light can be explained in this way, and strong support has come from Russia, where N. Kozirev, at the Crimean Astrophysical Observatory, has examined the 'dark' side spectroscopically and has announced that a particular form of nitrogen gas has been detected. It is significant that this kind of nitrogen is also a characteristic of auroræ in our own atmosphere.

Auroræ are associated with 'magnetic storms', or disturbances of the compass needle, which also arise from disturbances in the Sun. Some ingenious researches carried out by J. Houtgast, in Holland, have shown that Venus seems to have a powerful magnetic field. When the planet passes between the Sun and ourselves, at inferior conjunction,[1] its magnetic field might be expected to influence the streams of electrified particles coming from the Sun to the Earth, and Houtgast's analyses indicate that it actually does so. Probably the magnetic field of Venus is appreciably stronger than that of our own world, so that electrical phenomena there are only too likely.

[1] At most inferior conjunctions, of course, the lining-up is not exact – otherwise a transit would occur – but it is close enough to make Houtgast's researches valid.

Of course, the matter is by no means settled, and the auroral theory may turn out to be wrong after all; but at least it seems promising. Probably the Ashen Light is not a contrast effect, as some authorities still claim, because it can remain visible even when the bright crescent of Venus is blocked out of view by some device placed in the eyepiece of the telescope. On the other hand it is always elusive and hard to see, so that observations of it – either positive or negative – must be carried out with great care.

The only way to find out what the atmosphere of Venus is like is to make use of the spectroscope. This was done in the nineteenth century, but the first really reliable results did not come until 1932, when T. Dunham and W. S. Adams, at Mount Wilson Observatory in the United States, managed to prove that there is a tremendous amount of carbon dioxide over Venus.

There could be no doubt about the accuracy of this result, but it was both surprising and disappointing. Venus is virtually a twin of the Earth; why then should it not have a breathable atmosphere? Yet there seemed to be no free oxygen or water-vapour, and a thick, carbon-dioxide-rich mantle could not support advanced life-forms of the kind we know.

Analyzing a planet's atmosphere is by no means an easy process, because, for one thing, we have to reckon with the Earth's own air. The oxygen and water-vapour close to the ground leave their traces on the spectrum, and might be expected to mask the relatively weak effects of Cytherean oxygen and water-vapour. After all else had failed, two Americans, Commander Ross and C. B. Moore, went up in a balloon and carried out spectroscopic studies from high altitude. They were well above the densest part of the Earth's atmosphere, and they were able to detect water-vapour on Venus. This was in late 1959; in 1960 some theoretical researches carried out by B. Warner, in London, indicated that free oxygen gas might exist there too.

Evidently the atmosphere of Venus is not quite so alien as was believed until very recently. However, it is still unsuitable for Earth-type creatures, and we are uncertain about the nature of the clouds. Moreover, we must remember that we can study only the topmost part of the cloud-layer, and things may be very different underneath, though carbon dioxide is a heavy gas and would be expected to sink rather than to rise.

Spectroscopic work indicates that the upper layers are in violent motion. H. Suess has suggested that the clouds are made up of salts such as sodium chloride and magnesium chloride, produced by the drying-up of former oceans; R. Wildt believes that they are composed of formaldehyde, a compound of carbon, hydrogen, and oxygen; D. H. Menzel and F. L. Whipple hold the view that the clouds are simply H_2O, and that the surface of Venus is almost entirely covered with water. Now that water-vapour has been detected in the atmosphere, this last idea seems to be much the most plausible, but – as usual with Venus – we have no definite evidence.

Handicapped as we are, we can only guess at what the surface of Venus may be like. One view is that the whole planet is a dusty, lifeless desert, with constant gales blowing through the dense, unbreathable atmosphere; where the temperature is higher than that of boiling water, and the Sun's light is permanently screened. The other, due to Whipple and Menzel, is that there is almost no 'land' at all, and that the surface is covered with ocean.

Undoubtedly the temperature on Venus is high. Carbon dioxide, so abundant in the atmosphere, has a 'greenhouse' effect and tends to blanket in the Sun's heat; there are also radio observations – not of the same type as those made by Kraus – which lead to the same conclusion. But if the planet were desert, no water-vapour in the atmosphere would be expected, whereas we now know that water-vapour is plentiful. The balloon observations may not have disproved the desert theory, but they have certainly weakened it, and have opened up an interesting possibility concerning life on Venus.

Life on Earth began in the sea, more than 500 million years ago. In those far-off times our atmosphere contained more carbon dioxide and less oxygen than it does now; creatures such as ourselves could not have breathed it, and it was not until a later stage that plants spread on to the lands, removing much of the carbon dioxide and replacing it with free oxygen. Can there be a parallel with Venus, and can the seas on that rather peculiar world already support primitive life-forms? If so, Venus may be a world upon which life is just beginning.

When I first made this suggestion, some years ago, it was regarded (justifiably) as a wild guess. The detection of atmospheric water-vapour makes it perhaps more plausible, but it is still highly tentative, and may be completely wrong.

Meanwhile, we have every hope that space-research methods will

IV Venus. Change of phase and apparent diameter as the planet moves from behind the Sun, approaches the Earth and eventually passes between the Earth and the Sun. (Drawings by L. F. Ball)

Top left. 1956 February 26. 18 hours. 10 inch × 250.
Top right. 1953 January 23. 17 hours. 10 inch × 200.
Bottom left. 1959 July 18. 19½ hours. 10 inch × 200.
Bottom right. 1959 August 20. 18 hours. 10 inch × 175.

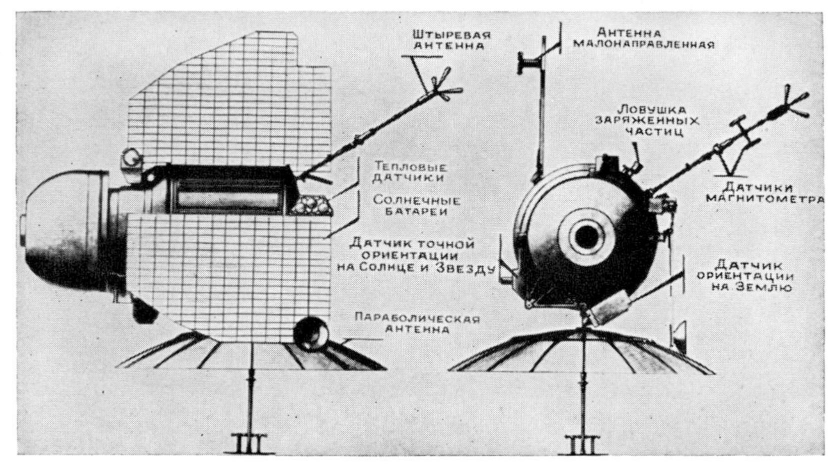

v The Venus Probe (the vehicle launched by the Russians in 1961). *Upper:* A photographic view. *Lower:* Diagrams of the arrangement of the probe

come to our aid. On 1961 February 12 the first full-scale 'Venus probe'[1] was launched by the Russians, and was expected to pass near Venus after a journey lasting approximately one hundred days. Radio contact with it was lost at a disappointingly early stage, but it seems that the vehicle approached Venus within 65,000 miles in mid-May, and then entered an orbit round the Sun. The chances of our

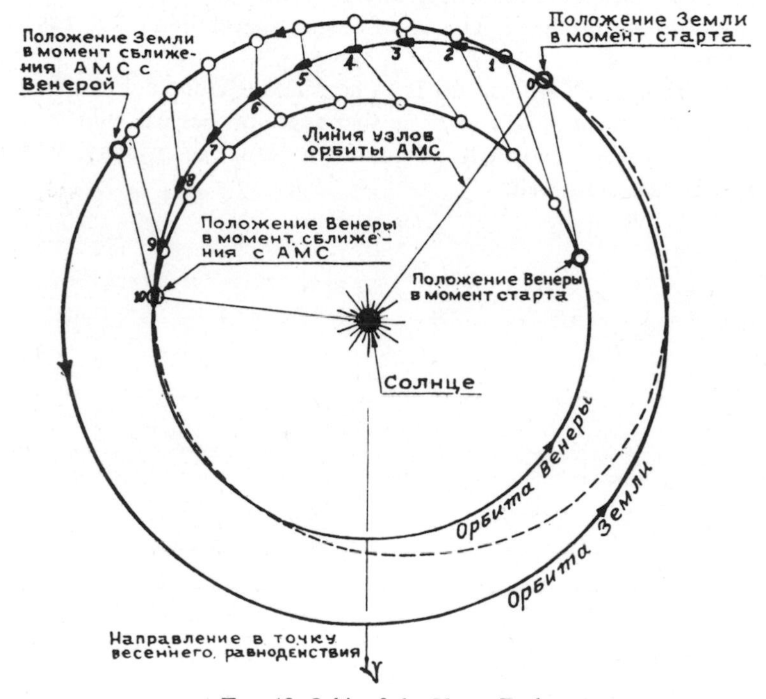

FIG. 18. Orbit of the Venus Probe

finding it again are negligible, and it was a partial success only, but it was only the first of many such probes which will be launched before long.

Lastly, what of the more distant future?

Until we have more positive knowledge, we cannot tell whether it will ever be possible to send men to Venus; but unless the surface

[1] The vehicle was nicknamed, rather irreverently, the 'Venusnik', but its official name is 'Lunik IV'.

conditions prove to be completely hostile, an attempt will presumably be made before many centuries have passed by. What the pioneers will find there, we simply do not know. They may land in a dusty desert, or they may find a watery world in which primitive aquatic life flourishes.

One sobering thought comes to mind. If colonies are established on Venus, men from our own planet may interfere with the evolution of indigenous life there. This is, of course, speculation – but it is not fantasy.

Meanwhile, all we can do is to continue telescopic and spectroscopic observation, and to hope that space-probes will add to our meagre store of knowledge. Venus is a planet of mystery, and it guards its secrets well.

Chapter 7

The Earth

THE THIRD MEMBER OF the Sun's family holds a special position in our view. This is natural; the Earth is our world, our home, and at first we find it difficult to realize that it is merely an ordinary planet, in no way remarkable.

The ancients found such an idea quite beyond their grasp, and up to less than five hundred years ago it was commonly believed that the Earth must be the centre of the universe. It was also thought that the Earth must be flat, but this mistake was put right by the Greeks, and – as we have seen – Eratosthenes of Cyrene made a remarkably accurate estimate of the size of the globe.

Actually, the Earth is not perfectly spherical. It is spinning on its axis, and so centrifugal force is most powerful at the equator. Consequently there is a definite bulge in the equatorial region, and the Earth has assumed the shape known technically as an 'oblate spheroid' – the shape of a very slightly flattened orange. However, the difference between the polar and equatorial diameters amounts to only 26 miles, which is not much when we remember that the mean diameter is over 7,900 miles. If we took a billiard ball and flattened it by an equivalent amount, the ball would still be usable for play. The less dense and quicker-spinning giant planets, particularly Jupiter and Saturn, show the effect much more obviously, and even a small telescope will show that they are flattened at the poles.

The Earth, then, is a normal planet – larger than Mercury or Mars, about the same size as Venus, far smaller than the outer giants. The orbit, too, is perfectly normal. The average distance from the Sun is 93,000,000 miles, and owing to the low orbital eccentricity this distance does not vary by as much as two million miles either way. The orbital velocity is about 18½ miles per second or 66,000 m.p.h. – a little more near perihelion, a little less at aphelion. It is strange to reflect that in a world where high speed has become a craze, Nature has outclassed our efforts completely without most of us being aware that we are being whirled round the Sun at all.

Oddly enough, the northern summer occurs when the Earth is near aphelion, at its farthest from the Sun – about 94,600,000 miles. This is because the axis of rotation is not perpendicular to the plane of the orbit, but is inclined at an angle of 23½ degrees. During northern summer, the north pole is tilted towards the Sun; six months later it

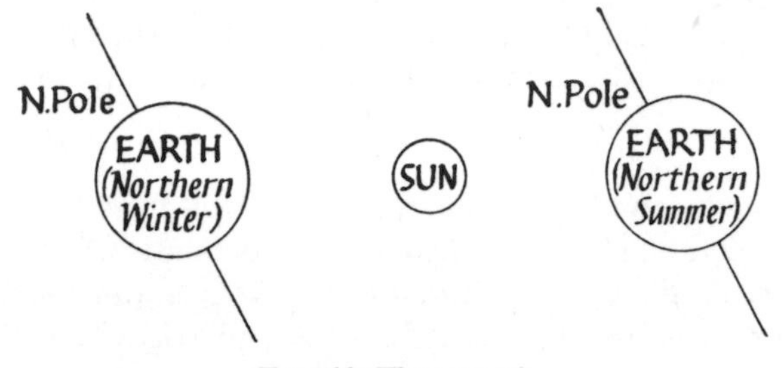

FIG. 19. The seasons

is the turn of the southern hemisphere, and it is winter in the north. Because the Earth is at its closest to the Sun in the southern summer, extremes of temperature are greatest south of the equator, with shorter but hotter summers and longer but colder winters; but the effect is not great, and is largely masked by the Earth's geographical peculiarities. The effect is much more marked upon Mars, where the axial tilt is similar but the orbit much less circular. Moreover, Mars has no oceans to moderate the extremes of temperature.

Considering that we have spent all our lives upon the Earth, we know surprisingly little about what lies beneath our feet. We can penetrate only a few miles downward – the deepest oil-well in the world, in California, stops at some 21,000 feet – and from then on we are reduced to indirect methods of investigation. We are not even sure how hot the Earth is near its centre.

Wells drilled into the ground show that the temperature rises by about one degree Fahrenheit for every 50 feet down, though the exact value varies for different localities. If this rate of increase continued to the Earth's core, the temperature there would be some 400,000 degrees F. – which seems most unlikely. Hence the temperature gradient cannot remain constant. It is now generally believed that the central temperature is only a few thousands of degrees.

Even this is hot enough to liquefy rocks under normal conditions, but conditions deep down in the Earth are not 'normal'. The pressure of the overlying layers is tremendous. At a depth of only 25 miles, for instance, the estimated pressure is 10,000 tons to the square foot, and although rock under such pressures would still technically be 'liquid', it would assume many of the properties of a solid. It would, however, still be able to flow. To make this clear, it may be helpful to consider the behaviour of pitch. A lump of pitch can be broken by a blow from a hammer, but if left to itself the pitch will flow in the same way as a very stiff liquid.

The depth at which the temperature becomes high enough for the rocks to flow in this way is taken to be the bottom of the Earth's crust. The region at the very bottom of the crust is known as the Mohorovicič Discontinuity[1] after the Jugoslav scientist who first drew attention to it. The thickness of the crust is not the same over all areas of the Earth. Under the continents it averages at least 30 miles, and is even thicker beneath the mountain ranges, but below the seas it is less, so that there may be only a mile or two of sediments and up to five miles of water above the Discontinuity.

There is one respect in which the Earth seems to be unusual in the planetary system. It is particularly dense. Taking water as unity, the Earth has a mean density of 5½; the values for Mercury and Venus are about 5, while the remaining planets are less substantial. (Saturn's mean density is actually less than that of water.) However, the surface rocks of the Earth have densities of between 2½ and 3½ only, and it is thought that there must be a heavy liquid core. The density near the centre of the Earth must be between 8 and 10.

The size of the core has been measured by means of earthquake waves, produced by the sudden slipping of the Earth's crustal rocks. In a normal earthquake, the actual shock occurs between 5 and 30 miles below the surface, and is termed the focus of the earthquake. The shock is transmitted to the surface directly above the focus, and this surface position is known as the epicentre.

Delicate instruments known as seismographs can measure earthquake shocks over distances of thousands of miles. Three types of waves are set up – primary or 'push' waves, secondary or 'shake'

[1] This is certainly a tongue-twisting name, and the Mohorovicič Discontinuity is often termed simply the 'Moho', which is easier to pronounce and is just as good.

waves, and finally the long waves which travel around the circumference of the globe and cause most of the material damage. The essential point is that while the primary waves will travel through liquid, the secondary waves will not. For any particular earthquake, therefore, there will be certain regions of the globe which will be protected from the secondary waves, which will be 'screened' by the liquid core.[1] Seismologists have been able to show that the core itself has a diameter of about 4,000 miles. The main constituents are thought to be iron and nickel-iron. The core is overlaid by a layer of stony material, which is in turn overlaid by a layer of rock known as peridotite. Above this comes the crust, made up largely of granite and other volcanic rocks.

If the Earth is made up in this way, it is only reasonable to assume that the other small planets – Mercury, Venus, and Mars, as well as the Moon – are built upon a similar pattern, though their lower mean densities probably indicate a smaller core.

This in turn is linked with the phenomenon of magnetism. Everyone is familiar with the ordinary pocket compass, and there can be no doubt that the Earth is a huge magnet, but we have to confess that we still do not know precisely why. However, it is very significant that iron, which is probably the main constituent of the core, is strongly magnetic.

Again there is a parallel with Venus, which is so very similar to our world in size and mass. Houtgast's experiments have shown that Venus has a strong magnetic field, and presumably it has a core comparable with that of the Earth. The Moon has a much lower overall density, and Russian rocket experiments indicate that its magnetic field is too weak to be measured – in which case any heavy core will be very limited in size. About Mars we have so far no precise information. Probably the magnetic field is much stronger than that of the Moon, but markedly weaker than those of the Earth and Venus.

Turning now to the Earth's surface, we are – literally – on firm ground. The chief peculiarity, compared with other planetary surfaces, is the presence of large sheets of water. The only other planets with a temperature at which surface water could exist are Venus and Mars. Venus may well have broad oceans, but there are certainly no extensive water-surfaces on Mars.

[1] There is no general agreement with regard to the composition of the inner part of the core, which may not be liquid.

The tides in our oceans, so important to shipping, are due mainly to the gravitational pull of the Moon,[1] which tends to heap up the water in a bulge underneath it, causing a corresponding bulge on the far side of the Earth. As the Earth rotates on its axis, the water-heap does not rotate with it, but tends to remain underneath the Moon. The result is that the water-heaps pass right round the Earth once a day; and since there are two heaps, each point on the Earth experiences two daily high tides. In practice there are many complications, but the main theory is simple enough. The Sun also has a tide-raising effect, and when the Sun and Moon are pulling in the same direction (i.e. at New and Full Moon), the tides are exceptionally strong.

These tidal effects would not be at all similar for Mars or Venus. The solar tides in the oceans of Venus would be quite powerful, but not so strong as our lunar tides. Any supposed Martian seas would be still and sluggish, since Mars is much farther away from the Sun, and the two dwarf moons would be unable to produce any appreciable tides.

One of the most interesting things about the Earth is its atmospheric mantle. Just as fish live at the bottom of an ocean of water, so we live at the bottom of an ocean of air, and the pressure of the overlying atmosphere is considerable. After all, the ordinary barometer, so familiar to all of us, is merely an instrument for registering changes in atmospheric pressure. Removal of this pressure would have most unpleasant consequences for us, quite apart from the fact that we would be unable to breathe. There is an excellent analogy with the case of a deep-sea fish which is abruptly brought to the surface of the water: it swells up and dies. It is not difficult to see why efficient pressurized space-suits will always be necessary upon airless worlds, and perhaps even on Mars.

The Earth's escape velocity is 7 miles per second. Air is made up of atoms and molecules flying about in all directions; if one of them happens to reach escape velocity, and is moving directly outward, it may escape into space. This is why worlds with feeble gravitational pulls, such as Mercury and the Moon, have been unable to retain appreciable atmospheres. Even on Mars, which has an escape velocity of 3·1 miles per second, the mantle is thin.

[1] For a rather more detailed account of the tides, see my book *Guide to the Moon*, Chapter 14.

It seems, however, that the Earth ought to be capable of retaining its atmosphere indefinitely; even hydrogen, lightest and quickest-moving of all gases, should be unable to get away. Yet the free hydrogen in the terrestrial atmosphere amounts to something like 0·01 per cent. in volume; two much heavier gases, nitrogen (78 per cent.) and oxygen (21 per cent.), make up between them 99 per cent. of the air – the remaining 1 per cent. being composed of argon and smaller quantities of carbon dioxide, hydrogen, and rare gases such as neon. Hydrogen is by far the most abundant element in the universe; what has happened to all the hydrogen which was once presumably present in the air-mantle? Some of it has combined with oxygen to form water, and some has combined with the surface materials; but even so, there is a vast amount of hydrogen unaccounted for.

According to one theory, the Earth must have been hot in the early stages of its separate existence. Increase of temperature means an increase in the speed of atoms and molecules, and it may well be that in its young, hot days the Earth lost not only most of its hydrogen, but also all the other gases originally present in the atmospheric mantle. The present atmosphere evolved mainly because volcanic action released a tremendous volume of gas from the Earth's interior.

Consequently, the Earth's atmosphere is of unusual composition. No other planet seems to possess a mantle containing much free oxygen. So far as we are concerned, oxygen is the life-giving gas; the nitrogen merely acts as a diluent, and though (needless to say) it is completely harmless it is of no direct use to us in breathing. It is probably true to say that we owe our existence to the presence of plants, which, by the process known as 'photosynthesis', remove excess carbon dioxide from the atmosphere and replace it with free oxygen.

Venus remains a problem, but there is not much free oxygen gas on Mars; and Jupiter and Saturn, with their high escape velocities, have hydrogen-rich atmospheres – because these massive worlds were able to hold on to their original mantles instead of losing them, as the Earth did. This means that life on any terrestrial pattern can be ruled out there.

From July 1957 to the end of 1958, scientists from over fifty nations – including Britain, the United States, and Soviet Russia – joined together in a general programme to find out more about the Earth.

The programme was known as the International Geophysical Year, though in fact it lasted for eighteen months, and had a wide range, including studies such as seismology, oceanography, and polar exploration. It was not the first combined programme – there had been two earlier Polar Years, one in 1882–3 and the other in 1932–3, devoted mainly to the Arctic and Antarctic – but it was undoubtedly the most ambitious. The results came well up to expectations, and the data accumulated will take at least two decades to analyze fully.

The artificial satellite launchings were included in the I.G.Y. programme, and in fact considerable attention was paid to the Earth's upper atmosphere. We must remember that normal flying machines, such as aeroplanes, are limited to the bottom few miles of the atmospheric mantle; at great heights only rocket vehicles will function at all.

Of course we could not exist without the atmosphere, since we would be unable to breathe. Yet the air-mantle has another property which is almost equally important to us: it protects us from various harmful radiations coming from space.

Some of these radiations originate in the Sun, which emits a vast quantity of ultra-violet – more than enough to prove fatal to all life on the Earth's surface unless it were screened. We must also consider the so-called cosmic rays, which are not really rays at all, but high-speed atomic nuclei. Cosmic rays are still something of a mystery, and most of them seem to come from far beyond the Solar System. The primary particles smash into the upper air, and are broken up; the fragments collide in turn, and the eventual result is that only harmless secondary fragments reach the ground.

Different in nature are meteors, which are small pieces of matter circling the Sun in the manner of dwarf planets. If a meteor approaches the Earth too closely it enters the resisting atmosphere, causing the familiar appearance of a shooting-star. Incandescence due to friction starts at about 120 miles above sea-level, and normal meteors are destroyed before penetrating as low as 50 miles. Even smaller particles or 'micro-meteors' are of too small mass to produce luminous effects.

Of the other terrestrial-type planets, Venus has an atmosphere which is fully effective as a meteor screen. This also applies to Mars. On the other hand, it seems that the tenuous atmospheres of Mercury and the Moon will be of no use at all in this respect, so that the surfaces of these worlds will be exposed to a continuous bombardment from space.

Now and then the Earth encounters a larger particle, which survives the complete drop to the ground and is then termed a 'meteorite'. One, found by Peary in Greenland, weighs 36 tons; the giant object still lying where it fell, in prehistoric times, at Hoba West in Africa has an estimated weight of 60 tons, while the meteorite[1] which hit Siberia in 1908 blew down pine-trees 20 miles away from the spot where it landed. There is a fundamental difference between bodies of this sort and ordinary meteors, which are mere grains of cosmic dust, and on the whole it seems that we cannot differentiate between a large meteorite and a small minor planet or asteroid. Fortunately such giants are rare, and there is no reliable proof that anyone has been killed by the fall of a meteorite, though several people have had narrow escapes.

During the I.G.Y., close studies were carried out of the beautiful auroræ or Polar Lights, which, as we have seen, are due to electrified particles sent out by the Sun. Auroræ are best seen in high latitudes, since the particles are drawn to the magnetic poles of the Earth (the geographical poles have nothing directly to do with it), but brilliant displays are sometimes more widespread. I well remember the aurora of 1938 January 26, when from my home at East Grinstead, in Sussex, the whole sky seemed to be on fire, and I thought at first that searchlights were responsible. Major displays were also seen on several occasions during the period of the I.G.Y. This was not purely a coincidence; every eleven years or so the Sun is particularly active, and the I.G.Y. had been deliberately timed to coincide with one of these 'solar maxima'. From places such as Iceland and North Norway, of course, auroræ are almost constantly visible when the sky is dark and clear, and this is also true of Antarctica.

The first object of the earth satellite launchings was to give us extra information about our own world. For instance, photographs covering large areas of the globe have proved to be of immense value in studying the weather systems. An unexpected but highly important discovery has been that of radiation belts surrounding the whole Earth; the Van Allen Belts, named in honour of the American scientist J. Van Allen – who played a major part in the studies leading

[1] Recent Russian investigations by K. Florensky and others indicate that the Siberian object was in fact a small comet, but proof is lacking at present.

to their detection – are closely bound up with phenomena of the Earth's magnetism. The Moon, with its weak magnetic field, does not seem to be associated with any comparable belt, and this is only to be expected.

Once artificial satellites had been sent up, it was natural for planetary and lunar probes to follow, but nothing of the sort would have been possible had not careful, preliminary work been carried out over a period of many years.

All that we know about the Earth tells us that it is a normal planet, quite undistinguished in the Sun's family. True, it is unusually dense; it has an unusual atmosphere, and it has a great deal of water – but Venus too may be largely ocean, while Mars must have at least a little moisture on its surface. Also, the Earth supports life, but even in this respect it may not be unique. We do not believe that other intelligent beings exist in the Solar System, but it is likely that there is plenty of 'vegetation' on Mars, and there may be primitive marine organisms on Venus.

From Mercury, the Earth would appear as a bright star, attended by a smaller one (the Moon); an observer on Venus, if he could penetrate his cloud-laden skies, would see the Earth as a splendid object – even the Moon would appear as brilliant as Venus itself does to us. To a Martian, the Earth would be an inferior planet, showing lunar-type phases, but from Jupiter our world would be hard to see at all, and from the more distant planets it would be hopelessly invisible.

We do not yet know the full story. How hot is the Earth inside? What is the real cause of its magnetism? And how did it come into being in the first place? These are only three of many problems which still await a final solution; and in trying to unravel them, we will also find out more about the other members of the Sun's family.

Chapter 8

The Moon

TO US, THE MOON appears as the most splendid object in the night sky. It is not surprising that ancient peoples regarded it as a god – or that moon-worship still continues today in a few backward countries. Yet the Moon is by no means important to the Solar System, to say nothing of the universe as a whole. It owes its great apparent brilliancy to the fact that it is exceptionally close to us.

The actual distance from the Earth varies to some extent, since the orbit is not perfectly circular, but averages about 239,000 miles. This is less than ten times the distance round the Earth's equator. Venus, the closest of the planets, is always at least a hundred times as remote, while Mars and the rest are more distant still.

The Moon is a relatively small body, a mere 2,160 miles in diameter, and with only $\frac{1}{81}$ of the mass of the Earth. Yet even these values make the Moon too large to be a normal satellite. It seems that instead of regarding the Earth–Moon system as a planet and a satellite, we would be more correct in describing it as a double planet.

A few figures will help to make this viewpoint clear. In the Solar System there are five known satellites – Io, Ganymede, and Callisto in Jupiter's system, Titan in Saturn's, and Triton in Neptune's – which are larger and more massive than our Moon. On the other hand, Jupiter, Saturn, and Neptune are themselves giants, whereas the Earth is a comparative dwarf. Triton has a diameter of about 3,000 miles and a mass twice that of the Moon, but this works out at only $\frac{1}{9}$ the diameter and $\frac{1}{750}$ the mass of its primary, Neptune. For the satellites of Jupiter and Saturn the differences are even greater. Titan, for example, has only $\frac{1}{4150}$ the mass of Saturn.

The Moon appears to be quite exceptional, and various theories have been put forward to account for its origin. According to G. H. Darwin, son of the famous naturalist Charles Darwin, the Earth and Moon used to be one body; quick rotation led to a large portion being thrown off from the equatorial zone, producing the Moon and leaving a hollow in the Earth's crust which is now filled by the Pacific Ocean. Unfortunately this idea, plausible though it sounds, has met with so many mathematical objections that it has been abandoned, and it now seems certain that the Earth and the Moon were never combined in one mass.

As was shown in Chapter 2, we still do not know quite how the Earth came into being. Yet we may reasonably assume that the Moon was born at about the same time and in the same region of space, so that it has always accompanied the Earth in its ceaseless journeying round the Sun.

Many textbooks state baldly that 'the Moon revolves round the Earth'. This is true enough, but it needs qualification. Strictly speaking, the Earth and Moon revolve round their common centre of gravity, much as the two bells of a dumbbell will do when twisted by their joining arm. Since the Earth is 81 times as massive as the Moon, this centre of gravity or *barycentre* is displaced towards the Earth – in fact it actually lies inside the terrestrial globe, and our simple original statement is good enough for most purposes so long as we remember that the mass of the Moon is far from negligible.

Everyone is familiar with the phases of the Moon. They must have been known from the earliest days of human history, and there are some curious old legends about them: the Slavs, for example, believed that the Moon, King of Night and husband of the Sun, faithlessly loved the Morning Star, wherefore 'he was cloven through in punishment, as we see him in the sky'. The regular changes from a thin crescent to a half, three-quarter or *gibbous* shape, full, and back to a crescent must indeed have seemed puzzling to our remote ancestors.

The diagram will make the situation clear. It is, of course, completely out of scale, but it is perfectly plain. Since the Moon has no light of its own, only half of it can shine at any one moment. In position 1, the dark side is turned towards us, and the Moon is invisible; this (not the thin crescent) is

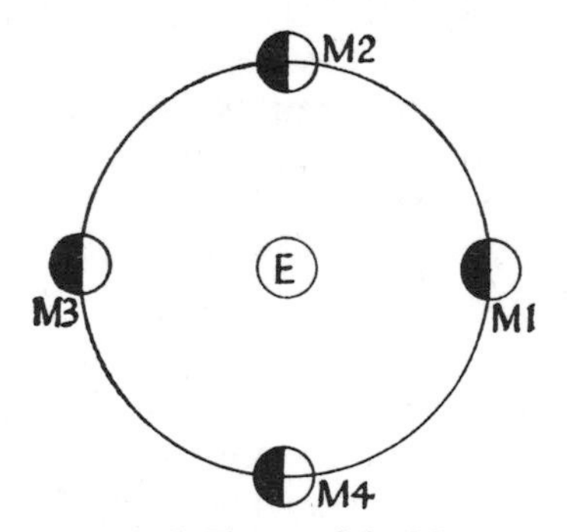

FIG. 20. Phases of the Moon

the astronomical 'new moon'. In position 2, half the sunlit face is turned towards us (First Quarter); in position 3, all of it (Full); and in position 4, half once more (Last Quarter).

The Moon takes 27·3 days to complete one revolution round the Earth, and this is a measure of the so-called *sidereal month*. However, the interval between successive new (or full) moons is rather longer than this, because the Earth is moving round the Sun, and this motion has to be taken into account. In the diagram, let us suppose that the Moon is represented by M, the Earth by E, and the Sun by

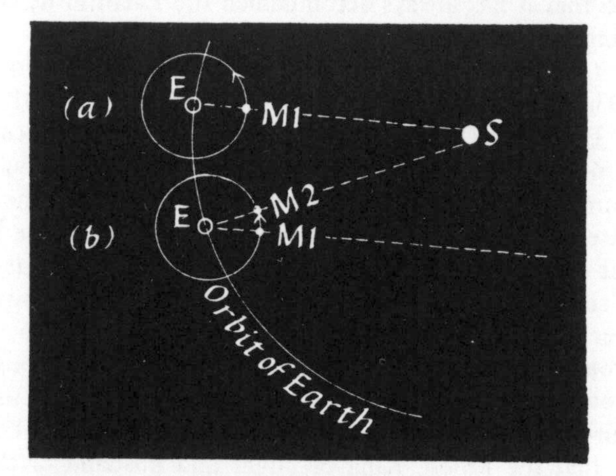

FIG. 21. Synodic Month

S. In the upper position the Moon is new at M1, since it lies between the Earth and the Sun. After 27·3 days the Moon has arrived back at position M1, but it is not now lined up with the Sun, because the Earth has moved along in its orbit. Only when the Moon has arrived at position M2 will it again be 'new'. The *synodic month*, or interval between new moons, is therefore 29·5 days instead of only 27·3.

At full phase, it sometimes happens that the Moon passes into the shadow cast by the Earth. The result is a lunar eclipse; all direct sunlight is cut off from the lunar surface, and the Moon becomes very dim until it emerges from the shadow. It does not disappear completely, as might be anticipated, because the Earth's mantle of atmosphere bends some light-rays on to the Moon.

Lunar eclipses may be either total or partial, and are more often seen than eclipses of the Sun.[1] They may be spectacular, and are always worth looking at. The next total lunar eclipses visible from Britain will take place on 1964 June 25 and December 19; 1968 April 13; 1971 February 10 and August 6; and 1975 November 18.

Even with the naked eye it is clear that the Moon's face is far from featureless. The legendary 'Man in the Moon' is formed by the dark and bright areas, but with the slightest optical aid the Old Man vanishes in a mass of detail. There are broad grey plains, together with mountain ranges, bright uplands, and thousands upon thousands of the walled circular formations known as craters.

The first map of the Moon was produced by Galileo in the early seventeenth century, soon after the invention of the telescope. Better charts were produced by his successors, and in 1837 came a really reliable map, the work of two German astronomers named Wilhelm Beer and Johann Mädler. Nowadays we have detailed charts; one, produced by the late H. P. Wilkins, is drawn to a scale of 300 inches to the Moon's diameter.

Photographic atlases have also been made. The latest is the work of G. P. Kuiper and his colleagues in the United States, and is of great value. Yet in some ways it demonstrates that photographic methods have their limitations. In Kuiper's atlas, many of the plates are insufficiently sharp to be used for precise measurement, and near the edge of the Moon the details are hopelessly blurred. This is no reflection on the American astronomers, but it does show that for this special kind of research the visual observer using a large telescope can still pick up more detail than any sensitive plate.

It was natural enough for early astronomers to regard the dark areas as seas and the bright regions as continents. Names were given accordingly, and are still used, generally in the Latin form; thus we have the Mare Serenitatis (Sea of Serenity), Mare Crisium (Sea of Crises), Oceanus Procellarum (Ocean of Storms), Sinus Iridum (Bay of Rainbows), and many others. Yet for centuries now we have known that the 'seas' are dry, and that there is not a drop of moisture anywhere on the Moon's surface.

The mountain ranges are lofty. The Apennines, bordering the vast Mare Imbrium (Sea of Showers), attain over 15,000 feet in places,

[1] To be accurate, solar and lunar eclipses are about equally numerous; but a solar eclipse is confined to a narrow strip across the Earth's surface, whereas a lunar eclipse, when it occurs, can be seen from an entire hemisphere. Any particular place on Earth will therefore see more lunar eclipses than solar ones.

and are splendidly seen with any small telescope. Even higher are the Leibnitz Mountains, in the far south of the Moon, which reach up to 30,000 feet. It is difficult to give exact values, because the absence of water on the Moon means that we cannot measure from 'sea-level', but at least the Leibnitz are of the same order as our own Everest. Since the Moon is so much smaller than the Earth, the lunar peaks are relatively much higher than terrestrial ones. Other important ranges are the Caucasus, Alps, Dörfel (not much inferior to the Leibnitz), and the Hæmus Mountains.

The whole lunar scene is dominated by the craters, which range from vast enclosures well over 100 miles in diameter down to tiny pits at the limit of visibility. Wilkins' map shows over 50,000 of them. In general, they are named after scientists of the past – a convenient albeit rather controversial system introduced by the Italian priest Johannes Riccioli, who drew a lunar map in 1651. Men such as Copernicus, Ptolemy, and Galileo are included, but some rather unexpected people seem to have found their way on to the Moon: for instance Julius Cæsar is there, presumably because he ordered an important reform of the calendar. There is a Birmingham on the Moon, named in honour of a nineteenth-century Irish astronomer, and there is even a crater called Hell. This rather startling name commemorates Maximilian Hell, a Hungarian scientist who lived two centuries ago.

Though some of the craters are deep, they are relatively shallow compared with their diameters. A typical formation, Alphonsus, is shown here in cross-section. It is over 70 miles across, and though the walls rise to several thousands of feet above the sunken floor the general section resembles a saucer rather than a deep, steep-sided well. Moreover, the wall does not tower high above the outer plain, and the slopes are surprisingly gentle.

The result of all this is that an observer standing inside a lunar crater would not feel in the least shut in. In many cases he would in fact be unable to see the encircling walls at all, since they would be below the horizon. It is worth noting that on the Moon, where the surface is more sharply curved than that of the Earth, the horizon will be relatively close at hand.

The depths of the craters – and, for that matter, the heights of the mountains – are measured by the shadow lengths. When the Sun is low over a crater, the interior will be filled with shadow, and the crater itself will be very prominent. This is particularly so when the crater lies on the *terminator*, or boundary between the daylit and night hemispheres. The terminator always appears rough and jagged, simply because the solar rays will fall on elevated points such as wall-crests and mountain-tops while adjacent valleys are still in darkness.

It is interesting to follow the progress of sunrise over various parts of the Moon. A crater which is very conspicuous one night, when it is shadow-filled, will become relatively obscure later, when the shadow inside it has decreased. At full moon, when the shadows are at their shortest, it may be hard to identify the crater at all, a fact which is borne out by the photographs given here. In fact, full moon is the very worst time to start trying to identify the craters. They are virtually without interior shadow, and moreover there is too much general glare. The most spectacular views are obtained around the time of half-moon.

Equally fascinating are the strange bright streaks of rays which come from some of the craters, particularly Tycho in the south and Copernicus in the east. These rays are best seen under high light, and at full moon are the most striking features on the entire disk. They cast no shadows, and so must be mere surface deposits, but their exact nature is still very uncertain.

We can do no more here than mention some of the minor features of the Moon – the swellings or domes, the deep cracks known as clefts or rills, and the chains of tiny crater-pits which give the general impression of strings of beads. There is a tremendous amount to see, and the amateur equipped with a moderate telescope will find enough to interest him over his whole lifetime. Meanwhile, let us turn to one of the most controversial questions concerning the lunar surface: What is the origin of the craters?

According to a theory proposed by the nineteenth-century German astronomer Franz von Gruithuisen, the craters were produced by meteoric impacts. We know of meteor craters on Earth, and there must also be many on the Moon. Also, under certain conditions impact craters may include central peaks which are superficially rather like the peaks found inside many of the craters on the Moon.

The meteor theory fell into disfavour for many years, but has been revived recently, and it is even suggested that the circular *maria* or seas may be of similar origin. However, there are several strong objections to the whole idea. The distribution of the craters is not random, as would be expected if the Moon had been subjected to a bombardment from space. For instance, when one crater breaks into another (as often happens) it is always the larger crater which is broken by the smaller, and not vice versa; I know of only two dubious departures from this rule. It is also significant that the craters, both large and small, tend to line up in chains, which suggests formations arising along a line of weakness in the crust rather than a sporadic bombardment from outside.

It is also important to look at the situation which is produced when two craters overlap, as shown in the photograph. The smaller crater intrudes into the larger, and so must be younger. If it had been produced by a falling meteorite, it would surely have led to a tremendous 'moonquake' which would have shaken down the already existing features over a wide area. Yet nothing of the sort is ever observed.

The arguments still continue, and will probably go on until space-research methods enable us to analyze the lunar crust directly. It seems likely, however, that although many of the pits must be meteoric, the larger craters and the *maria* were produced by internal forces rather than by impact.

There are some objects on the Moon which are undoubtedly volcanic. They take the form of rounded hills with central pits, and look very like ordinary terrestrial volcanoes. Between 1952 and 1958 I made a prolonged search for these features, using the great refractor at the Observatory of Meudon, and found a total of over fifty, so that they are not so uncommon as used to be thought.

The main craters are different in character, and are quite unlike volcanoes of the Vesuvius type. However, there are some terrestrial vulcanoids – near Richat in Africa, for instance, and in the Lake Mývatn area of Iceland – which bear a remarkable resemblance to lunar formations.[1]

It seems that the lunar features may be regarded as 'volcanic' if we use the term in a broad sense, and the craters may well have been produced by an uplift-and-subsidence process. This also applies

[1] In 1960 I carried out some practical surveys of the craters Hverfjall and Lúdent, in Iceland. The similarity with lunar forms was unmistakable; Hverfjall even has a central peak.

to the circular, well-defined seas such as the Mare Crisium, which are in the nature of exceptionally large craters. It even seems that a certain amount of activity may linger on, though the Moon is a world where major outbreaks cannot have occurred for many hundreds of millions of years.

Mädler, senior author of the first reliable lunar map, considered that the Moon must be a dead, changeless world, where nothing ever happens. Nowadays a rather different view is held. Two cases of suspected change, in Linné and in Alphonsus, are certainly worthy of special mention.

Linné lies on the Mare Serenitatis (Sea of Serenity). Up to 1843 it was drawn by all observers as a deep, prominent crater; the diameter was given as 8 miles, and there was no feature of importance anywhere near it. In 1865 Julius Schmidt, a German who had achieved wide fame for his studies of the Moon, reported that Linné no longer existed in its old form; it had become a much smaller pit, standing on a swelling and surrounded by a whitish deposit. This is the modern appearance. It is unlikely that any change has taken place since 1865, but it may well be that something – perhaps a small 'moonquake' – occurred between 1843 and 1865. It is possible, of course, that Linné never looked like a large crater, and that the old observers were mistaken, but the whole question certainly provides food for thought.

No such doubts attach to the activity in Alphonsus, which is much more recent and which has been confirmed photographically.

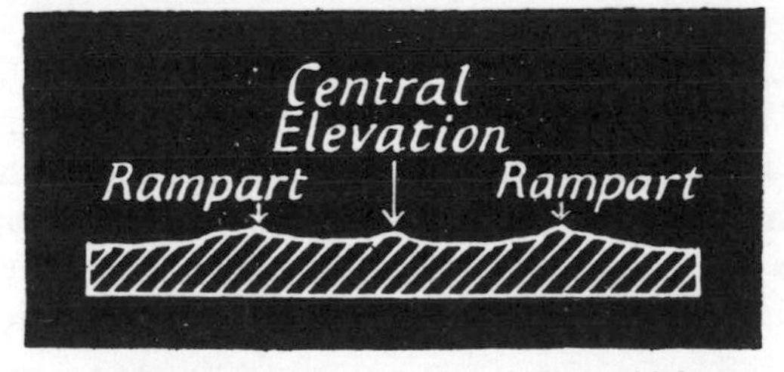

FIG. 22. Cross-section of the lunar crater Alphonsus

Alphonsus is a large walled plain, over 70 miles across, lying near the apparent centre of the Moon's disk; it is bounded by the even larger Ptolemæus on the north, and by Arzachel on the south. Inside Alphonsus are some curious dark patches which have been suspected of alteration in shape. There is also a central elevation, together with a system of clefts.

On 1958 November 3 the Russian astronomer N. A. Kozirev, working with the 50-inch reflector at the Crimean Astrophysical Observatory, was studying the Alphonsus area. His attention had been drawn to it by the reports made by D. Alter, of the United States, that the crater floor was sometimes subject to 'obscurations' which might be due to a very tenuous, possibly temporary, atmosphere. Suddenly Kozirev saw a reddish patch near the central peak of Alphonsus. As he watched, the patch moved very slowly and began to fade.

Fortunately, Kozirev was able to take photographs which showed that hot carbon gas was being emitted from the central peak area. The photographs – or, rather, spectrograms – were conclusive that a disturbance had taken place, and it is likely that the temperature rise amounted to about 2,000 degrees, though this has been questioned. The whole phenomenon lasted for only about half an hour, and was very minor by terrestrial standards, but at least it showed that the Moon is not completely inert.[1]

Most of the essential differences between the Moon and the Earth are due to the fact that the Moon is virtually without atmosphere. There is nothing surprising in this, since the lunar escape velocity is only 1½ miles per second, and any dense mantle which may have existed in the remote past has long since leaked away into space. Yet we must be wary of supposing that no trace of atmosphere remains.

A simple observation will set an upper limit to the atmospheric density. In its journey across the sky, the Moon sometimes passes in front of a star, and occults it. On these occasions the star goes on shining steadily until the moment of occultation, when it snaps out instantaneously. Were there any appreciable atmosphere around the Moon's limb, the star would flicker and fade for several seconds before vanishing – as actually happens during occultations of stars by Venus.

Tests of this sort can show that the lunar atmosphere cannot have a density of more than $\frac{1}{10000}$ that of the Earth's air at sea-level.

[1] The whole matter gave rise to great controversy. During a visit to the U.S.S.R. in 1960 I discussed it with Kozirev, at the Crimea, and saw the original spectrograms, so confirming my original view that the observation was completely valid and that no errors of interpretation or fact were involved.

More delicate and less direct methods of research indicate that the real density is probably more in the region of $\frac{1}{100000}$ – considerably less than was believed only a few years ago. If this is so, the lunar mantle will be useless as a meteor screen, and will be unable to shield the Moon's surface in any way.

Assuming that the Moon does possess a very thin atmosphere, it may well be that the main constituent gases are helium and argon, produced by the decay of radioactive materials in the lunar rocks, but at the moment we have no positive proof.

Since we must discount the lunar atmosphere as a moderating influence on temperature, we can see at once that the Moon must have a most uncomfortable climate. At noon on the equator, the temperature rises to about the boiling point of water (212 degrees F.), while at midnight a thermometer would register something like minus 250 degrees F. These figures are reasonably accurate, since it is possible to measure the quantity of heat sent to us by the Moon.

The nights are equally cold in all areas, but the day temperatures are less violent away from the equator. In the region of the northern crater Plato, for example, a thermometer would never rise above 140 degrees F., and at the lunar poles the rocks are always below freezing point. This state of affairs will certainly have to be borne in mind when choosing the landing-site for the first true 'Moon-ship'. The most suitable area is likely to be somewhere in the vast Mare Imbrium (Sea of Showers), though it is as yet too early to make definite forecasts.

There is no local colour on the Moon; bright blues, reds, and greens, for instance, simply do not occur. It looks as though the surface must be either bare rock, or else overlaid with ashy or dusty material – partly meteoric, partly volcanic. The curious bright rays from Tycho and similar craters may be caused by ash ejected from the craters at a late stage in lunar activity, but once again we have no proof, and moreover we are still uncertain as to the nature of the surface coating.

There must be a certain amount of meteoric dust, and according to a theory put forward by T. Gold this dust may be miles deep, so that any rocket landing on the Moon would sink out of sight almost at once. However, Gold's theory has not met with much support, and it seems much more probable that the surface layer is only a few inches deep.

One important series of observations has been carried out by radio astronomers. Heated bodies emit radiations of all kinds – not only visible light, but also long-wave radiation which may be collected by radio telescope – and the Moon is no exception. The lunar radio waves come from below the visible surface, and so allow us to study conditions a few inches underneath the upper layer. In particular, it has been found that the temperatures several inches below the visible surface are not nearly so extreme as those measured in the normal manner, so that the surface material must be good at insulating heat.

It is quite possible that the surface layer is composed of material similar to slag. Russian astronomers tend to believe that the Moon is covered with a layer of pulverized material with grains ranging from 3 to 10 millimetres in diameter, below which lies solid volcanic rock.

At all events, we are unlikely to find any living thing on the Moon. It used to be thought that lowly organisms might survive in a few favoured spots – particularly in some of the craters such as Eratosthenes (at one end of the Apennine mountain chain) and Alphonsus, which contain strange dark patches. Aristarchus, the brightest crater on the whole Moon, contains some peculiar dark streaks which also were attributed to 'vegetation' of some sort. Nowadays, all the evidence points to a contrary view. It is not impossible that some primitive organisms may exist on the Moon; but we have no evidence that they do, and there is a great deal of evidence that they do not.

In passing, it is worth mentioning that some authorities believe that we can actually handle pieces of matter which have come from the Moon. These are the mysterious tektites, which are found in various well-defined areas on the Earth's surface. Tektites seem to have been heated twice, and it is suggested that they may have been hurled out from lunar volcanoes, suffering a second heating as they plunged to the ground through the Earth's atmosphere. Opinions vary, but it is becoming more and more likely that tektites have an extra-terrestrial origin, and the idea that they come from the Moon has met with wide support.

Finally, let us come to one of the most brilliant chapters in the story of modern science – the exploration of the 'other side of the Moon'.

We have seen that the planet Mercury always keeps the same face to the Sun, because its revolution period is the same as its axial rotation period (88 days). The Moon behaves in the same way with respect to the Earth. There is a slight 'rocking' motion, because the orbital speed changes according to the distance from the Earth; moreover the lunar orbit is appreciably inclined, so that we can see for some way beyond the mean limb alternately in the north and in the south. The result of these two *librations* is that we can examine 59 per cent. of the total surface, though of course only 50 per cent. can be seen at any one moment. The remaining 41 per cent. is never turned towards the Earth, and remained unknown until very recently.

Even the regions near the Moon's edge or *limb* are difficult to map. Though the general form of the craters is circular, formations near the limb are foreshortened, and the craters appear elliptical. Look, for instance, at the great enclosure Pythagoras. It has a diameter of about 100 miles, and is almost perfectly circular, but to us it looks like a long, narrow ellipse. Moreover, the changing libration means that its distance from the limb varies between certain well-defined limits, so that sometimes it appears more foreshortened than at others.

The foreshortening effect is well illustrated in the case of the Mare Crisium (Sea of Crises). The general impression is that the plain is elongated in a north–south direction, but actually the diameter is slightly greater when measured from east to west.

Hansen, a last-century Danish astronomer, suggested that the Moon might be 'lop-sided' in mass, so that its centre of gravity was displaced from its centre of figure, and all the air and water had been drawn round to the hidden side. This attractive idea is so obviously unsound that it has never met with any backing from scientists (though plenty from astrologers, flying saucer enthusiasts, and others of their kind). There seemed no reason to suppose that the hidden regions were basically different from those which we have always known, but the only way to obtain positive proof would be to send a camera-carrying rocket to find out.

In the latter part of 1958 American space-scientists planned their 'Pioneer' vehicle, which was designed to pass beyond the Moon, photograph the hidden regions, and then send the pictures back to Earth by means of complex television techniques. Unfortunately the

Pioneer launchings were not successful, though two of the vehicles rose to around 70,000 miles before falling back to destruction in the Earth's atmosphere.

Then, in 1959, the Russians sent up three vehicles, all outstanding in their various ways. In January came Lunik I, which passed within 4,000 miles of the Moon and sent back valuable information: it confirmed, for instance, that the lunar magnetic field is negligible. Lunik I never returned. It continued its journey, and presumably it will go on circling the Sun for millions of years to come, though we have no chance of contacting it again.

Lunik II, launched on September 12, landed on the Moon thirty-six hours after it left its Russian rocket base. Apparently it came down in the region of Archimedes, in the Mare Imbrium, and must have destroyed itself on impact. Signals from it were still being received a few seconds before the crash came, and further important data were secured.

On October 4, exactly two years after the ascent of the first artificial satellite, came the momentous flight of Lunik III – or, as the Russians themselves called it, 'the automatic interplanetary station'. This time the idea was not to hit the Moon, but to go round it. By October 7 the vehicle was beyond the Moon, at a distance of about 38,000 miles

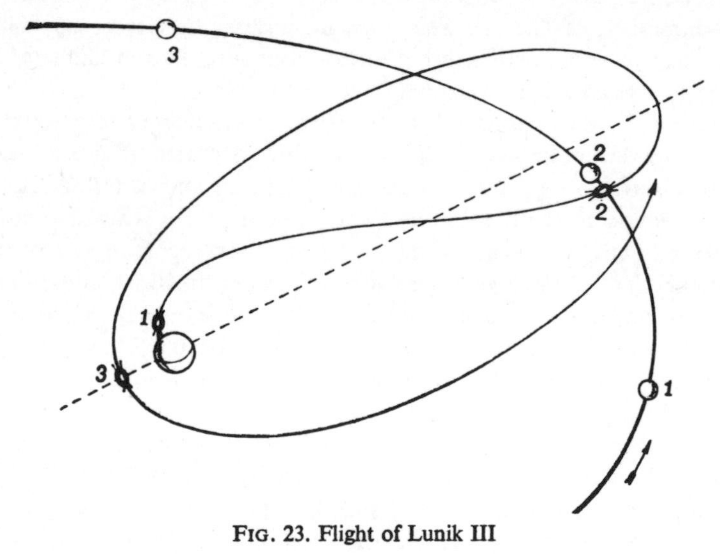

FIG. 23. Flight of Lunik III

VI View of the Full Moon

VII The group of craters consisting of Ptolemæus, Alphonsus, and Arzachel. Ptolemæus is the large crater at the bottom (north) of the photograph; Alphonsus and Arzachel above it, and Albategnius, another great walled plain, to the left

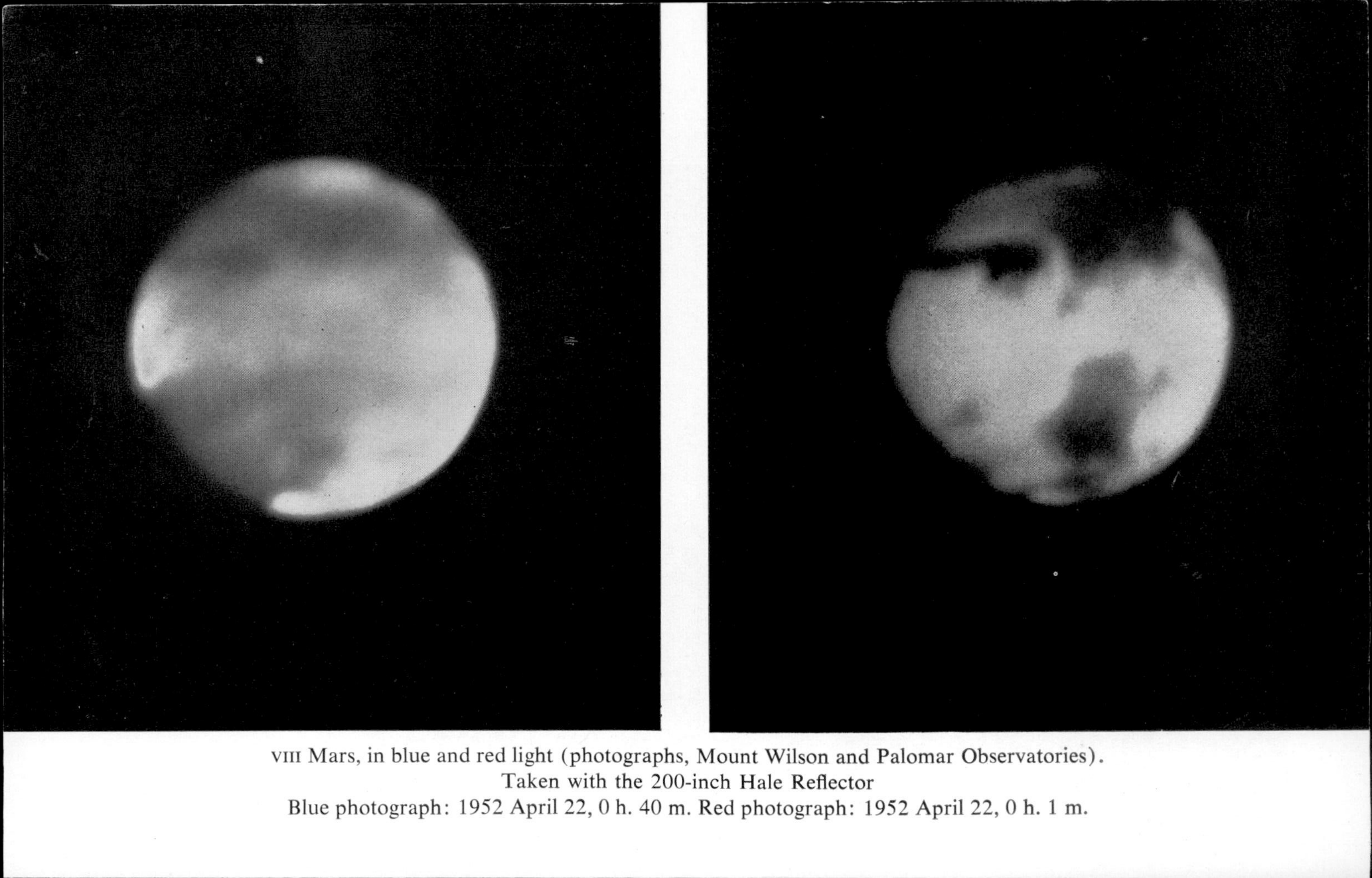

VIII Mars, in blue and red light (photographs, Mount Wilson and Palomar Observatories).
Taken with the 200-inch Hale Reflector
Blue photograph: 1952 April 22, 0 h. 40 m. Red photograph: 1952 April 22, 0 h. 1 m.

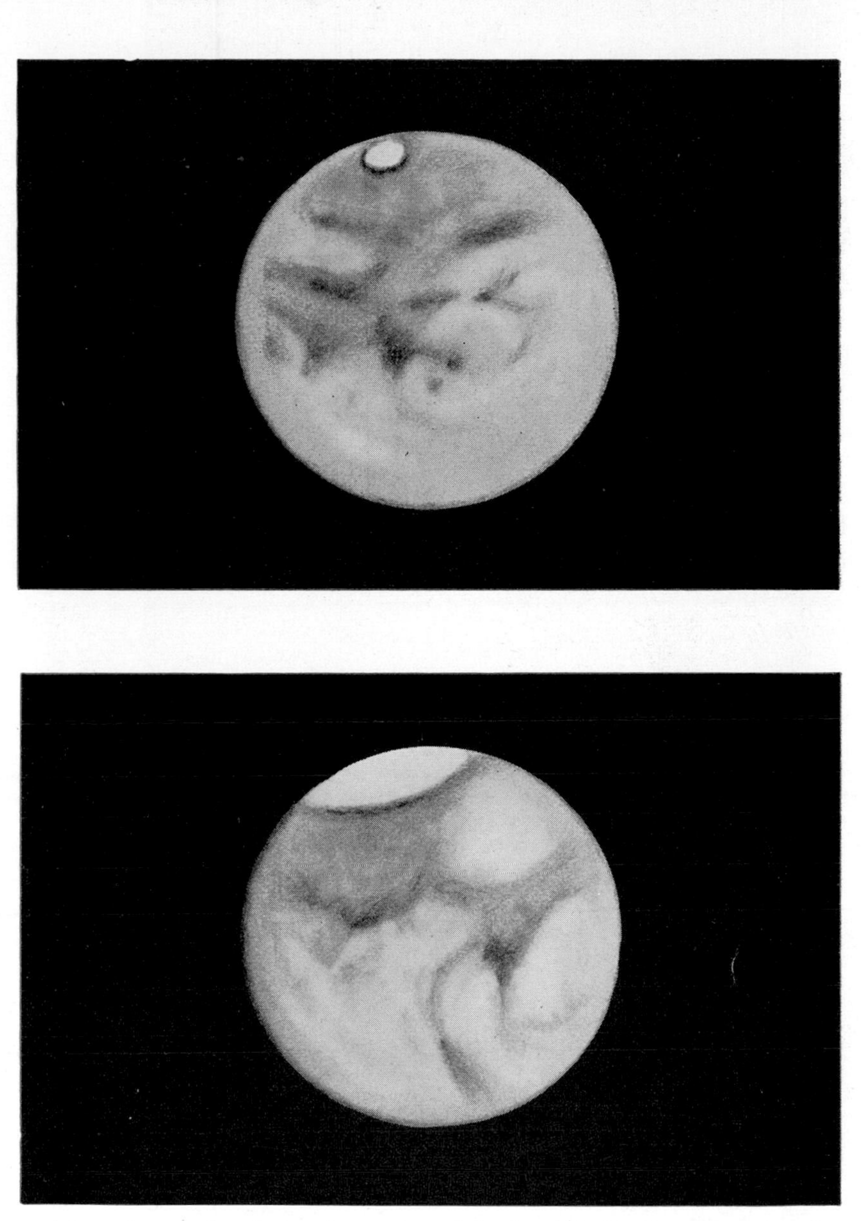

IX Mars. Seasonal variation in the size of the South Polar Cap. (Drawings by L. F. Ball)

Top. 1941 October 23. Central Meridian 60°. 10 inch × 350.
Bottom. 1941 June 24. Central Meridian 260°. 10 inch × 300.

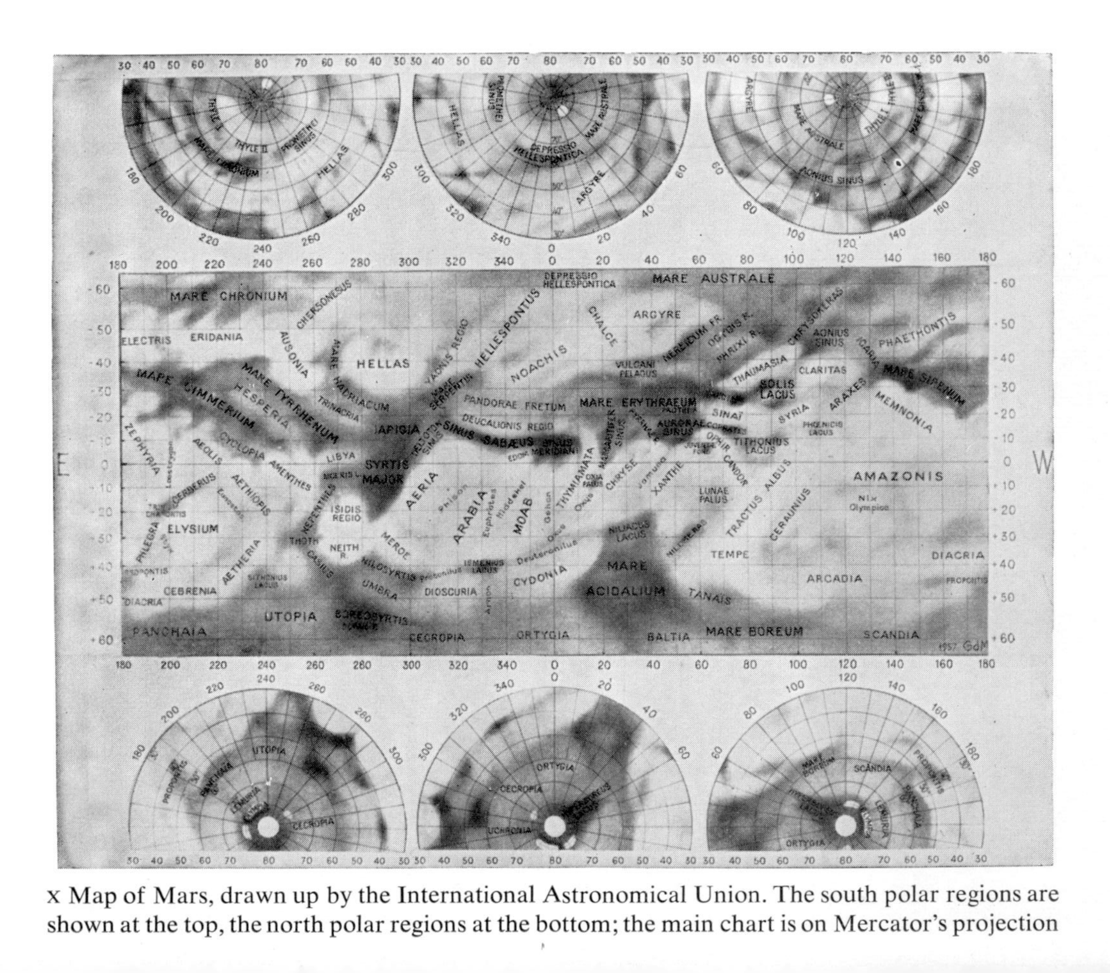

x Map of Mars, drawn up by the International Astronomical Union. The south polar regions are shown at the top, the north polar regions at the bottom; the main chart is on Mercator's projection

from the lunar surface; the cameras were brought into action, and 70 per cent. of the hidden side of the Moon was photographed. Later, when the Lunik had come back to the vicinity of our own world, the pictures were successfully sent back by television.

The results surpassed all expectations. The first photographs to be released showed part of the familiar hemisphere, with features such as the Mare Crisium, together with large areas of the previously unknown side. As had been predicted, large 'seas' were comparatively rare, but there were smaller plains such as the well-marked feature which Soviet scientists christened the Mare Moscoviæ (Sea of Moscow), together with craters, mountains, and other expected features.

By early 1961 the thirty or so photographs obtained from Lunik III had been closely analyzed by a team of Russian astronomers, and a detailed chart of the new regions was published under the editorship of Y. N. Lipski. Correlation with the visible hemisphere was carried out largely by use of the limb-charts prepared by H. P. Wilkins, in Britain, years earlier. Lipski's map shows hundreds of craters, and there can no longer be any doubt that the Moon is barren and lifeless over its entire surface. No doubt clearer pictures will be obtained before long, and it should also be possible to land vehicles on the Moon sufficiently gently to avoid damaging their instruments, so providing us with a true lunar transmitting station; but nothing can ever dim the glory of Lunik III, which represented one of the greatest astronomical triumphs of all time.

The final fate of the vehicle itself is uncertain. Its transmitters suddenly ceased to operate, and all contact with it was lost. A straightforward power failure may have been responsible; but when I was in Moscow in 1960, and was discussing the problem with the scientific team there, I found that the general view was that the Lunik had been hit and damaged by a meteor. There is certainly nothing improbable in this, since meteors are common in space, and even minor damage would be enough to put the transmitters permanently out of action.

Progress in space-research is now so rapid that we are being no more than soberly optimistic when we claim that men will reach the Moon before many years have passed by. The pioneers will land upon a world which is strange indeed – without atmosphere, without water, and without life in any form. Neither can we expect to find evidence of former life. The Queen of Night has been barren throughout her long existence; no beings have ever survived on her grey rocks, no footsteps have ever echoed across her plains. The Moon's awakening will be left to men from our own world.

Chapter 9

Mars

OF ALL THE MEMBERS of the Sun's family, there can be no doubt that the red world Mars, first of the planets which we find beyond the orbit of the Earth, is one of the most interesting. In some ways it is not so very unlike the Earth, and there is every chance that it supports life in some form.

When at its closest to us Mars may approach the Earth to within 35,000,000 miles, so that it is then much nearer than any planet apart from Venus. It outshines even Jupiter, and is striking not only because of its brilliance but also because of the strong red colour which led the ancients to name it after the God of War.

Mars is a comparatively small planet. It is 4,200 miles in diameter, and has little more than one-tenth the mass of the Earth. The escape velocity is only about 3 miles per second, and, as might be expected,

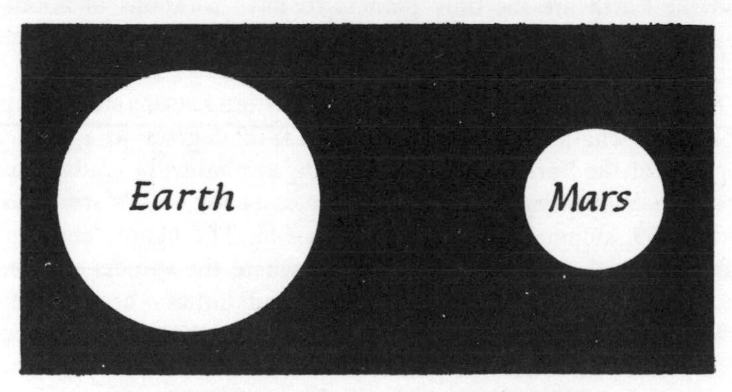

FIG. 24. Comparative sizes of the Earth and Mars

the atmosphere is relatively thin. We can thus have a more or less clear view of the surface features, and our knowledge of Mars is much more extensive than in the case of cloud-covered Venus.

On the other hand we must not expect too much. Even when at

its nearest, Mars is always at least 140 times as distant as the Moon, so that even with giant telescopes we can never have a better view of Mars than we can have of the Moon with low-power binoculars. The broad details are obvious enough, but we cannot see nearly as much as we would like to do.

Mars has always been regarded as one of our first astronautical objectives. Unmanned probes to it will probably be launched during the next few years, and there is every reason to suppose that men will be able to go there before the end of the twenty-first century, though it is dangerous to make firm predictions. At any rate, there is no harm in making controlled speculations; so what will our hypothetical Martian colonists find?

First, the length of the 'year' will be unfamiliar. The mean distance between Mars and the Sun is roughly 141,000,000 miles, and the sidereal period amounts to 687 terrestrial days, so that a man who is thirty years old by Earth reckoning will be only sixteen according to the Martian calendar. However, the rotation period is of the same order as our own – a mere forty minutes longer; the exact value is 24 hours 37 minutes 22·6 seconds. This is certainly accurate to within a tenth of a second, since the hard, well-defined markings on the disk make the rotation period easy to measure. So far as we know, Mars and the Earth are the only planets to have rotations of about 24 hours; Mercury, Venus, and Pluto spin more slowly, the giant planets much more rapidly.

Neither would the colonists find the Martian seasons strange, apart from their length. The axial inclination is 25 degrees, as against 23½ degrees for the Earth, so that conditions are basically similar. In the northern hemisphere of Mars, winter lasts for 160 Martian days, spring 199, summer 182, and autumn 146. The figures are slightly different for the southern hemisphere, where the winters are longer and colder and the summers shorter and hotter – because Mars' orbit is of appreciable eccentricity, and the southern summer occurs near perihelion, when the planet is at its closest to the Sun and is moving most rapidly in its path.

The temperature of the Martian surface has been measured with reasonable accuracy, and conditions prove to be fairly tolerable. The old idea of Mars as a frozen world seems to be very wide of the mark. In the tropics, the summer temperature may rise to as much as 70 degrees Fahrenheit. The nights are certainly bitter, and a thermometer would register well below minus 100 degrees Fahrenheit, but some of our own polar regions are almost equally uninviting in the depths of winter. G. de Vaucouleurs has justly stated that the general temperature of Mars 'is not very different from that of the Earth, and only a little more rigorous on the average'.

Unfortunately Mars presents its own observational problems, due principally to the fact that its orbital velocity – 15 miles per second on the average – is only a little less than that of the Earth, so that oppositions occur at intervals of 780 days or so instead of taking

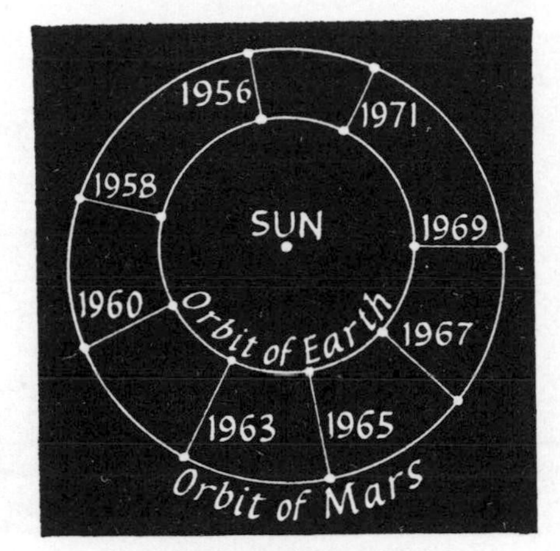

FIG. 25. Oppositions of Mars

place each year. There were oppositions in 1956, 1958, and the end of 1960, but in 1955, 1957, and 1959 Mars was so far away that no useful observations of it could be made even with large telescopes.

Moreover, not all oppositions are equally favourable. This is because of the marked eccentricity of the planet's orbit. The distance from the Sun varies between 128,500,000 miles at perihelion to 154,500,000 miles at aphelion, so that when opposition occurs near aphelion – as happened in 1948, and will happen again in 1965 – the minimum distance from the Earth is over 60,000,000 miles. We will have to wait until the year 1971 for another really favourable opposition.

It can be seen that Mars often shows a slight phase, and can appear the shape of the Moon a few days before or after full. For obvious reasons, Mars never appears as a half or a crescent.

To compensate for the long intervals between oppositions, we can at least study the solid surface. We are not reduced to occasional glimpses, as in the case of Mercury, and neither are we baulked by the dense layers of 'cloud' which prevent our finding out much about Venus. Even a small telescope will show something, while a moderate instrument will reveal a reddish-ochre disk upon which are darker patches. These dark patches are permanent, and can be mapped. The most conspicuous of them is known as the Syrtis Major, and is rather triangular in shape. It was drawn in recognizable form by Christiaan

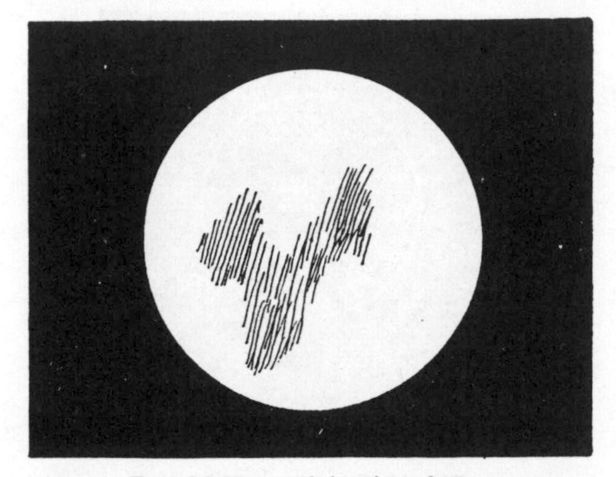

FIG. 26. Huygens' drawing of Mars

Huygens as long ago as the year 1659, and has evidently not altered appreciably since then. In fact, it has probably been unchanged for many millions of years.

Originally the reddish-ochre areas were thought to be deserts, while the dark patches were regarded as seas. The first idea is basically correct if we use the word 'desert' in a broad sense, but the second is definitely wrong. Mars is desperately short of water, and there are no large oceans anywhere on the planet. Recently, the Russian astronomer V. Davidov has suggested that underground seas exist, and that the surface is covered with ice; but this does not seem to be in good accord with the temperature measurements, and although Davidov's theory is interesting it is not supported by any firm evidence.

However, there must be at least some moisture on Mars. There is every reason to suppose that the bright white polar caps, well seen in a small telescope when the planet is near opposition, are due to some icy or frosty deposit. This is logical enough – after all, the Earth has extensive snow-caps – but the arguments about it were not really settled until 1948, when G. P. Kuiper, in the United States, reported spectroscopic observations of water ice there. Previously it had been thought that the caps might be due to solid carbon dioxide, even though nobody had suggested a really good reason why carbon dioxide should accumulate in such a way.

Despite this, it would be wrong to jump to the conclusion that the poles of Mars are coated with vast icy deposits similar to those of Greenland or Antarctica. Like the caps of the Earth, the Martian white areas shrink during the spring and summer and re-form during the winter, but their rate of decrease alone shows that they can hardly be more than a few inches thick. At its greatest extent, the southern cap may measure 3,000 miles across; yet in midsummer it may vanish entirely. The northern cap never quite disappears, but neither is it ever so large as its southern counterpart at maximum. This is because the temperature extremes in the northern hemisphere are less.

It is tempting to say that the polar caps shrink because they melt with the arrival of warmer weather, but this may not be true. We are used to ice and snow turning to water when the temperature rises well above freezing point, but conditions are different on Mars; the atmospheric pressure is less, so that water boils at a much lower temperature – probably about 77 degrees Fahrenheit, as against 212 degrees for the Earth at sea-level. Instead of melting in the conventional way, much of the polar deposit on Mars may sublime, i.e. pass directly from the solid to the gaseous state. This may account for the whitish cloudy veils often seen above the caps.

It has even been supposed that the caps may be due to nothing more than a layer of hoar-frost. In any case, the depth cannot be great, and this sums up the whole problem of Mars: shortage of water. The planet has developed more rapidly than the Earth, and has lost more of its atmosphere, so that any former oceans have presumably dried up. If all the liquid locked up in the two polar caps could be released at once, the total volume of water would not be sufficient to fill the Black Sea.

Earlier observers did not realize the seriousness of the water deficiency on Mars, but nowadays we are well aware of it; and unless

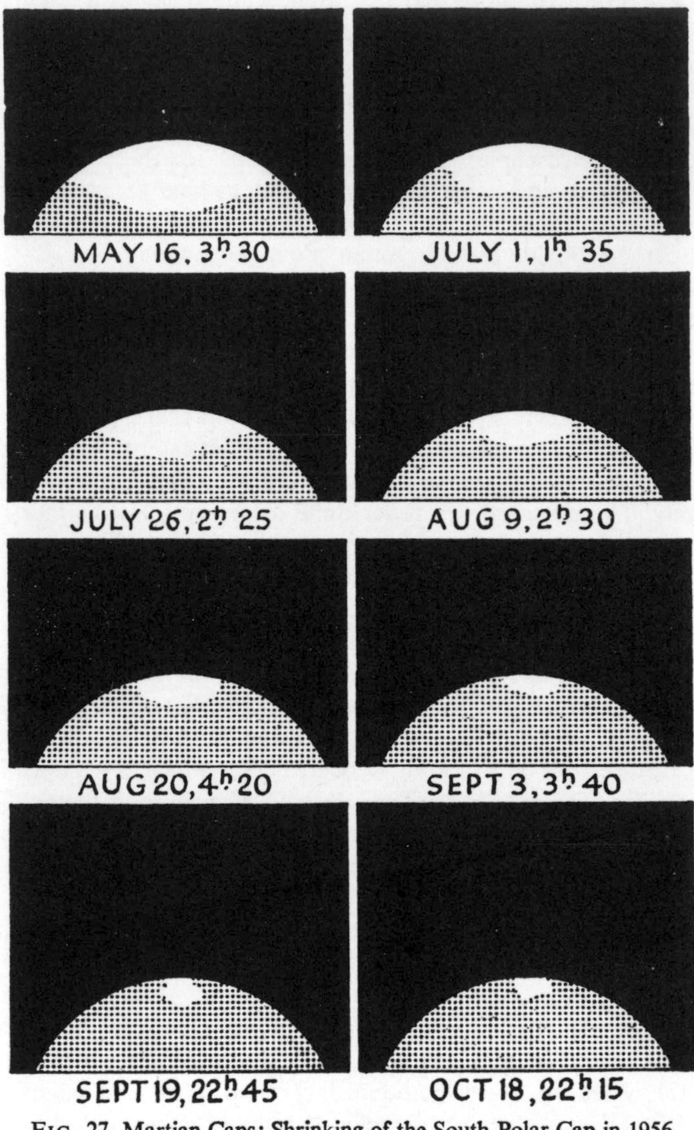

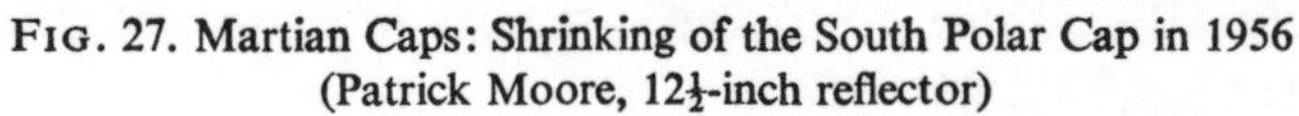

FIG. 27. Martian Caps: Shrinking of the South Polar Cap in 1956
(Patrick Moore, 12½-inch reflector)

Davidov's theory proves to be correct, future colonists from Earth will have difficult problems to solve on this score alone.

It is possible, however, that temporary marshes may be found here and there. When a polar cap is shrinking quickly, a dark 'collar' is often seen round it. This cannot be dismissed as a mere contrast effect, as has often been stated. Kuiper, for instance, studied it under excellent conditions in 1950, using the great 82-inch reflector at the McDonald Observatory in Texas, and 'found it black . . . The rim is unquestionably real; its width is not constant, and its boundary is irregular'.

It is reasonable to assume that this collar is due to marshiness round the border of the cap; damp ground always appears darker than dry ground. The collar shrinks steadily as the cap retreats, however, so that the marshiness must dry up quickly, and it is most unlikely that anything in the nature of a true polar sea ever forms. Occasional pools of water are as much as the colonists can ever hope to find.

As a cap shrinks and a certain amount of moisture (whether in liquid or in gaseous form) is released, the darker areas in the temperate zones seem to be affected. A 'wave of darkening', as de Vaucouleurs has described it, spreads from the poles in the direction of the equator; the markings become more distinct, and there are changes in colour. Some of the dark regions respond more noticeably than others, but we would expect local conditions to play their part in a seasonal cycle, just as is the case on Earth.

Vegetation might be expected to behave in this manner; it would surely develop as soon as moisture reached it from the shrinking polar caps. For this reason, it has been widely supposed that the dark patches are in fact due to living matter. The suggestion seems to have originated with a paper written by a French astronomer, Liais, in 1878, and most modern astronomers follow it. A few, however, disagree – most notably V. V. Sharonov, of Leningrad, who believes the areas to be mountainous regions undergoing erosion.

One theory which met with wide support for many years was put forward by Svante Arrhenius of Sweden. According to Arrhenius, the areas were covered with hygroscopic salts, i.e. salts which absorb moisture and darken in the process. Admittedly this would explain the famous seasonal cycle, but the slight depth of the polar caps indicates that not nearly enough moisture would be made available, and it is now thought that the idea is definitely untenable. An alternative suggestion by the American astronomer D. B. McLaughlin, that the areas are produced by ash ejected regularly from active volcanoes and spread out by winds, seems to have nothing whatever in its favour.

We have to agree that the hypothesis of living matter is much more plausible, but the term 'vegetation' is rather misleading, since we have no real idea of what form the living matter may take. It may well be unlike anything which we find on our own world. In any case it will not be highly developed, and advanced plants such as flowers and trees seem to be out of the question. Meanwhile, some important work has been carried out by W. Sinton in the United States, who has studied the infra-red spectrum of the dark areas of Mars and has found absorption bands which are probably due to organic compounds. This does not prove that life exists on Mars, but it does make it seem likely.

A simple argument – which, strangely enough, nobody seems to have put forward until E. J. Öpik did so fairly recently – is that if the dark areas had no regenerative powers, they would long ago have been overlaid by material blown from the 'deserts', so that the whole surface of Mars would have become reddish-ochre. In other words, there must be something to push the 'desert' material out of the way. Again this indicates growth, which can come only from living organisms.

Despite its distance and its small size, Mars has been well charted. Although the main outlines of the dark areas do not alter from year to year, smaller details do. Sometimes a patch will undergo a slow, progressive change until it has altered its shape completely, after which it may change back again with equal slowness; sometimes there will be a comparatively rapid change, followed after a period of years by an equally rapid return to the old form. One region, the so-called Solis Lacus (Lake of the Sun), is notorious for its alterations. On the generally accepted theory, these changes may be due to the spread and retreat of the organisms responsible.

Although the dark areas are not seas now, it is not impossible that they were seas many millions of years ago, when Mars was a world with abundant air and water. Support for this idea is given by the fact that the dark patches seem to be lower-lying than the deserts; and as Martian winds are quite appreciable, we find extra support for Öpik's suggestion that nothing but living matter could prevent the lower-lying areas from being covered up and taking on the reddish hue of the rest of the planet.

It is also significant that the dark areas are appreciably warmer than the deserts. This, again, is only to be expected.

On Mercury and the Moon, perhaps on Venus also, there are mountains and valleys; but Mars is not a hilly world. Of course, it is not completely level – we cannot picture a planet with a totally smooth surface, unless, as Davidov believes, it is covered with ice – but great chains of peaks such as the terrestrial Himalayas or the lunar Apennines are definitely absent.

The most recent work on the problem of Martian relief has been carried out by A. Dollfus at the Pic du Midi, who has tried to detect shadows cast by peaks near the terminator of Mars when the planet shows its maximum phase. So far he has been unsuccessful, which is hardly surprising. It is rather like trying to find the shadow of an ant-hill when observing from an aeroplane flying thousands of feet above the ground.

The shrinking polar caps, however, give us some information. As they decrease, their borders become irregular; salients and notches appear, as would be expected upon a non-level surface. We would anticipate that the white deposit would persist longest in the highest regions. From studies of this kind, Dollfus has calculated that there are plateaux at least 3,000 feet high in the polar regions, while one or two isolated white patches in more temperate zones may be due to the same cause. However, Mars has two-sevenths of the Earth's surface area; if the peaks were as high, relatively, as ours, they would tower to something over 10,000 feet – which they certainly do not. We seem here to have evidence of violent erosion in the past.

Although the polar caps and the dark areas combined cover vast tracts of the Martian surface, most of the planet is reddish-ochre in hue. From early times, these expanses have been regarded as deserts. Yet they are certainly not sandy; sand is the accumulation of soil and rock débris produced by running water – and running water cannot be expected anywhere on Mars.

B. Lyot, who paid great attention to the problem, considered that Mars must be coated with 'a dusty cover analogous to that which covers the lands of the Moon', but it may well be that the lunar covering is due mainly to volcanic ash (together with meteoric dust), and there is not much likelihood of extensive volcanic activity on Mars. Another suggestion is that the deserts are dust, coloured by metallic salts such as iron oxide – or, to give it its common name, rust. This would explain the reddish colour, and also the scarcity of oxygen in the Martian atmosphere, but the most recent work indicates that the surface coating is more likely to be made up either of limonite or else of brownish, fine-grained felsite.

At all events, the reddish-ochre areas seem undoubtedly to be 'deserts', far less productive than the darker tracts. Unlike our Saharas, they are cold, and no welcoming oases will break their monotony. They must be incredibly dismal and lonely.

Most of the differences between conditions on Mars and the Earth arise from two basic causes. The first is that Mars is much further from the Sun, and so receives less warmth. The second is the relative thinness of the atmosphere. The ground pressure is believed to be about 85 millibars, or 2½ inches of mercury – equal to the pressure in the Earth's atmosphere at a height of 56,000 feet above sea-level, well above the limit where men or advanced animals can breathe. We can see, then, that for this reason alone there can be no beings of our own type upon Mars.

Neither is the composition of the atmosphere favourable for the existence of animal life. According to an estimate by de Vaucouleurs, the Martian mantle consists of 98·5 per cent. by volume of nitrogen, 1·2 per cent. of argon, 0·25 per cent. of carbon dioxide, and less than 0·1 per cent of oxygen. For the Earth's atmosphere, of course, the values are accurately known: 78·1 per cent. nitrogen, 0·9 per cent. argon, 0·03 per cent. carbon dioxide, and 20·9 per cent. oxygen.

In each case, then, the most plentiful gas is nitrogen (N_2). Obviously it is harmless – otherwise we could not survive on Earth – but so far as we are concerned it acts mainly as a diluent, and we depend upon the life-giving gas oxygen. There is very little free oxygen in the Martian atmosphere, even though de Vaucouleurs' figure of 0·1 per cent. may prove to be something of an underestimate. Neither is there much moisture, though a certain amount must presumably exist.

The trouble about nitrogen is that the common form of it is not easy to detect with a spectroscope, and we have to depend upon rather indirect evidence. Recently three American astronomers, C. C. Kiess, H. K. Kiess, and S. Karrer, have suggested that the atmosphere of Mars contains poisonous oxides of nitrogen, in which case any sort of life on the planet would have to be ruled out. Yet on the whole it seems that the composition suggested by de Vaucouleurs is the most likely, and although Earth-type creatures could not breathe on Mars they would not find it toxic.

There is another trouble to be faced, too. The boiling point of a liquid is affected by pressure; the lower the pressure, the lower the boiling point – which is why water will boil at only 187 degrees Fahrenheit on the top of Everest, though at sea-level it must be heated to 212 degrees. At a height of 63,000 feet above the Earth, the boiling point of blood would be lowered so much that anyone unprotected by a vacuum-suit would find his blood boiling inside him. The results would be rather unfortunate, to put it mildly. Airmen who fly at such altitudes are safeguarded by pressure-cabins, and usually wear special suits as well, just in case of accidents.

As we have seen, the pressure at the surface of Mars is about the same as would be found 56,000 feet above the Earth. Yet this figure may not be accurate, and if the pressure is slightly lower than expected it may prove to be impossible for any Earthman to walk about in the open without wearing a protective suit. So far as the blood-boiling nuisance is concerned, Mars seems to be a borderline case.

Another interesting feature of the Martian atmosphere is the so-called 'violet layer', which blocks out short-wave radiations coming from outside. Despite its name, the violet layer is not visible in an ordinary telescope, and it certainly does not look violet!

Light of short wavelength is violet or blue; if the wavelength is relatively long, the colour is red. It is a general rule that 'the longer the wavelength, the greater the penetrating power'. The blueness of our sky gives a striking proof of this; the short-wave light coming from the Sun is spread about all over the heavens, because it is scattered by the air-particles, while the yellow and red light comes more or less straight through.

Under normal conditions, no surface details are recorded on Mars if a photograph is taken using blue or violet light only. This is because the planet's atmosphere blocks the short-wave light, and the photograph shows only the top part of the mantle. With red light, the surface details are recorded, because the longer wavelengths can slice through the atmosphere and reach the ground.

The Martian atmosphere is very effective at stopping the short waves. There seems to be a definite layer which is almost opaque to the blue and violet, and it is this which has become known as the violet layer. Its exact nature is not known, but apparently it lies at a height of about eight miles above the planet's surface.

Violet light has the shortest wavelength of the rays which affect our eyes. Light of still shorter wavelength (ultra-violet) cannot be seen, though it can be felt and photographed. In small quantities it is beneficial – every modern hospital has ultra-violet lamp equipment – but in larger quantities it is dangerous to living matter. The Sun sends out a tremendous amount of this lethal radiation, but fortunately for us a layer of ozone in our atmosphere gives full protection. Ozone, incidentally, is nothing more than a special form of oxygen gas.

Whether or not the violet layer on Mars is made up of ozone, it seems to be a good screen against the Sun's ultra-violet bombardment. In this respect, at least, future explorers from Earth will have nothing much to worry about.

Yet now and again the violet layer clears away for a spell, and photographs taken with short wavelengths show the surface features. One of these clearings took place in May 1937, and was studied by the American astronomer S. L. Hess, who found that during the absence of the layer there was a halt in the seasonal cycle of the dark areas. Hess concluded that since the ultra-violet screen had been temporarily withdrawn, the Martian plants were being damaged by the short-wave radiations from the Sun, so that their development was stopped. Much the same thing was found in 1941, when there was another clearing. We seem here to have further indirect evidence that the dark patches are due to something which grows.

Rainfall must be unknown on Mars, but clouds are seen frequently. They are of three kinds. The first, the 'blue' clouds, are best seen in light of short wavelength, and are high-altitude phenomena, possibly in the nature of hazes. Secondly there are the 'white' clouds, which lie between 4 and 16 miles above the ground, and seem to be made up of ice crystals, so that they resemble the fleecy cirrus clouds so common in our own skies. And lastly we have the 'yellow' clouds, which sometimes cover large areas of the planet, and appear to be nothing more nor less than dust-storms.

The white clouds may be conspicuous at times, and their movements give us at least a rough clue as to the wind-circulation on Mars. Studies of them indicate that the winds are gentle, and seldom exceed 20 knots, though we cannot be at all precise.

The yellow clouds occur at a much lower level, and may completely hide the surface below. This happened, for instance, in 1909, and again in 1911, when a vast cloud in the southern hemisphere persisted for several months. The most likely explanation is that dust is whipped up from the deserts by storms of the cyclone variety. Inside a cyclone system the wind speeds might be considerable, but there would be no evidence of this as seen from Earth, since the weather system as a whole would move slowly across the Martian surface.

We are at a loss to account for the yellow clouds if we decide to reject the idea of dust-storms. Volcanic eruptions have been suggested, but here again we run into grave difficulties. Mars has reached too late a stage of development for violent vulcanism to be expected. It is also noticeable that volcanic activity seems to be bound up in some way with water – all terrestrial volcanoes lie fairly near the sea – and, as we know, there is not much water left on Mars.

At times the whole atmosphere of Mars appears to be strangely hazy. In 1956, for instance, the opposition distance was reduced almost to its minimum value of around 35,000,000 miles, and it was expected that even small telescopes would show considerable detail on the disk. This did not happen, and in consequence some amateur observers jumped to the conclusion that there must be something wrong with their telescopes. Actually, the Martian atmosphere was to blame. I remember that on September 12, almost at opposition, I made an observation under excellent seeing conditions and with the help of a large telescope (the 24-inch reflector at Meudon), and could see practically no markings at all. In 1958, and again in 1960–1, the planet was not so close, but its atmosphere had cleared, and much more detail could be recorded.

Great interest was aroused in late 1951 by an unusual observation made by a Japanese astronomer, Tsuneo Saheki. At 21 hours G.M.T. on December 8, he detected a small, starlike spot over the area known as Tithonius Lacus, not far from the south pole. During the next few minutes it increased in brilliancy and became larger, finally fading out after an hour or so. Clearly something uncommon had happened, and various somewhat unlikely explanations were put forward in the Press. One London daily paper went so far as to suggest that the Martians were trying to communicate with us by means of flashing mirrors, and another considered it possible that an atomic bomb had been exploded. The landing on Mars of a large meteorite was also suggested, but even a giant body such as the famous Siberian meteorite of 1908 would have been quite unable to produce such a glow, and on the whole it seems reasonable to assume that the phenomenon was due to some unusual cloud formation.

We can see, then, that the Martian atmosphere is of the greatest interest. Admittedly it is unbreathable, but it will serve as a meteor-screen, and (usually) as a protection against solar ultra-violet, so that in this respect as well as others Mars is much less hostile than Mercury or the Moon.

Many books have been written about Mars, and this survey of the main features is necessarily sketchy and incomplete. Before we turn our attention to the so-called 'non-natural' features, however, something must be said about the two tiny moons, perhaps the most extraordinary satellites in the Solar System.

Up to 1877 it was believed that Mars, like Mercury and Venus, was moonless; but in that year Asaph Hall, at Washington, discovered two dwarf attendants which were subsequently named Phobos ('Dread') and Deimos ('Terror'), after the two servants of the mythological War-God. Dean Swift, in his immortal *Gulliver's Voyages*, had already predicted them, and so had Voltaire in his curious novel *Micromégas*, but it is quite certain that they had never been seen before 1877. Even when Mars is best placed, they are very elusive. I have glimpsed Phobos with my 12·5-inch reflector, and both satellites with a 15-inch, but not easily.

Phobos and Deimos are very small indeed – so small that their diameters are rather uncertain. Phobos is around 10 miles across, and Deimos 5, so that if such a thing were possible it would take only a few hours to walk right round either. Actually, however, it would be impossible to 'walk' there in the conventional manner. The surface gravities are so low that a man would weigh less than an ounce.

Even to an observer on the Martian surface, the satellites would appear far from brilliant. Deimos, indeed, would look like a rather large and dim star.

Both Phobos and Deimos move in a most peculiar fashion. They have been described as 'dynamical nightmares', and with good

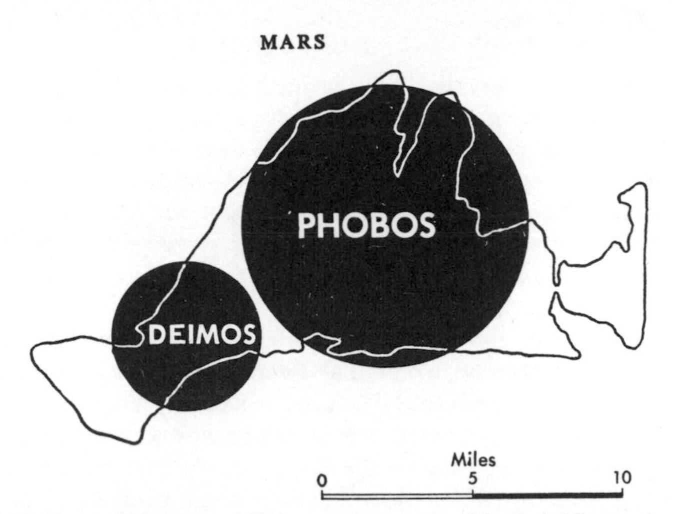

FIG. 28. Sizes of Phobos and Deimos, compared to Martha's Vineyard

reason. Phobos is perhaps the odder of the two. For one thing, it is remarkably close to Mars – a mere 3,700 miles above the surface; only about as far as from New York to Paris – and it goes round the planet in 7 hours 39 minutes, which is only one-third the length of the Martian day. To an observer on Mars, Phobos would appear to rise in the west and set in the east, crossing the sky in only 4½ hours, and passing through more than half its cycle of phases. If it rose as a thin crescent, it would be nearly full before it set. The interval between successive risings would be about 11 hours. For long periods, of course, it would be eclipsed by Mars' shadow.

Deimos is equally strange in its own way. It is much farther out – about 12,500 miles above the surface, equal to the distance between England and Australia – and its revolution period is 30 hours, which is longer, but not much longer, than the 24½-hour Martian day. As Mars spins, therefore, Deimos almost keeps pace with it, falling behind only slowly. It remains above the Martian horizon at any one place for 2½ days at a stretch, passing through its cycle of phases twice.

These bewildering little moonlets undergo all sorts of eclipse phenomena. They pass in and out of the shadow of Mars; Phobos may occult Deimos; and a Martian observer would see frequent solar eclipses – or should they be called satellite transits? When Phobos passes in front of the Sun, as it does some 1,300 times each Martian year, it covers less than half the solar disk, and the eclipse is a rather hurried affair, since it lasts for only 19 seconds. Deimos produces 120 eclipses a year, but covers only a small fraction of the Sun, and takes two minutes to pass right across. As neither satellite looks large enough to cover the whole disk of the Sun, the Martian astronomers – if they existed! – could never have the privilege of seeing the Sun's outer surroundings, the corona and the prominences, with the naked eye.

Not so long ago, considerable interest was aroused by a suggestion made by a Russian writer that Phobos and Deimos might be artificial, and were probably hollow. Amazingly enough, some newspapers treated this weird idea seriously, and a paper on the subject was solemnly read before the British Interplanetary Society. At any rate it is an attractive theory, even if about as likely as the age-old hypothesis that our own Moon is made of green cheese.

But though we must certainly dismiss the idea that Phobos and Deimos are artificial, can we say the same about those famous (or perhaps notorious) features, the Martian canals?

The story of the canals began as long ago as 1877, the year in which Hall first detected the two satellites. Mars was well placed for observation, and the Italian astronomer G. V. Schiaparelli made close studies of it. He was using a good 8¾-inch refractor, the Italian skies are clear and dust-free, and there is no doubt that Schiaparelli himself was a first-class observer and draughtsman, so that in 1877 and the following two oppositions (those of 1879 and 1881) he was able to draw up charts of the planet far superior to any previously made.

In addition to the well-known light and dark areas, and of course the polar caps, Schiaparelli noticed other features which puzzled him considerably. The ochre tracts appeared to be crossed by numbers of fine, dark lines. These lines were invariably straight, or at least great circle tracks; they ran from dark area to dark area; they never stopped abruptly in the middle of a desert, and altogether they looked quite unlike anything else in the Solar System. Schiaparelli called them 'canali' – or, in English, 'channels'. Where they crossed, as they often did, were small darkish patches which were later christened 'oases'.[1]

[1] To be strictly accurate, some of the canals had been indicated by earlier observers – including Beer and Mädler, who produced the famous map of the Moon and also studied Mars. However, Schiaparelli was the first to draw the canals in large numbers, and to describe them in detail.

It is often said that Schiaparelli himself was convinced that the features were natural, and that the very name 'canal' is a gross mistranslation. This view is not entirely correct. Schiaparelli was careful to keep a strictly open mind. He certainly believed that the canals were great ditches in the planet's surface, utilized – whether naturally or not – for the passage of water from the icy poles to the arid desert regions. Towards the end of his career, indeed, he wrote that 'their singular aspect has led some to see in them the work of intelligent beings. I am very careful not to combat this suggestion, which contains nothing impossible'.

No other observer managed to see the canals in 1877 or 1879, and Schiaparelli's drawings were still unconfirmed when, in 1881, he came across another extraordinary fact. Some of the canals, previously seen as single lines, turned abruptly into twins. In place of the original canal, two canals were seen – strictly parallel throughout their length and similar in every way. Sometimes one component occupied the original site; sometimes the two components lay to either side of the track of the original canal.

Not all the canals showed this curious doubling or 'gemination'. Only a certain number of canals behaved in such a manner. When doubling took place, it did so suddenly and completely. A canal which had been recorded as single on one night might appear as a perfect pair the next. Neither were the separating distances the same; some pairs were divided by as much as 400 miles, others by as little as 50.

It is hardly surprising that Schiaparelli's reports were treated with a good deal of scepticism, and for some years it was generally believed that he had been the victim of some curious illusion. But in 1885 two French astronomers, Perrotin and Thollon, using the large refractor at the Observatory of Nice, announced that they had confirmed Schiaparelli's observations. A. S. Williams, in England, followed; and gradually others too began to see canals, until the network was regarded as more or less established.

Schiaparelli's failing eyesight forced him to give up all practical work in 1890, but by then two other astronomers had come very much to the fore – Percival Lowell and W. H. Pickering. Lowell founded the famous observatory at Flagstaff, in Arizona, principally to study Mars, and between 1894 and his death in 1916 he attacked the canal problem with immense energy. Altogether he made many thousands of drawings, and recorded over seven hundred canals.

Lowell was quite definite in his views. He considered that the canals were artificial, constructed by intelligent beings to convey water from the ice-capped poles through to the waterless desert regions. To Lowell, therefore, Mars was the abode of life even more advanced than our own. In his words: 'That Mars is inhabited by beings of some sort or other we may consider as certain as it is uncertain what those beings may be.'

It is quite true that many of the observed phenomena could be explained in this way. The canals would be at their faintest in the Martian winter, increasing in visibility with the release of water from the caps; the doubling of some canals could also be accounted for, as if one channel proved inadequate to cope with the available supply another channel, close to the first, could be opened at short notice. Pumping stations would be necessary, though the building of a planet-wide irrigation system on this scale would be a difficult matter, even when we take into account Mars' low gravity and lack of major chains of peaks.

Lowell never suggested that the canals were channels of open water. To be visible at all across a minimum distance of 35,000,000 miles, they must be 30 or 40 miles broad; and water channels of this size would suffer crippling losses by evaporation if they were open to the atmosphere. In any case, the polar caps certainly do not contain enough water to fill tremendous ditches hundreds or even thousands of miles long. Lowell pictured a canal as being a comparatively narrow water channel, possibly piped, flanked on either side by a strip of cultivated land.

Lowell's maps of Mars were indeed most peculiar. He showed the canals as extremely narrow, perfectly straight and very numerous, crossing not only the deserts but also the dark areas. In fact, his canal system was much too regular to be the work of Nature. Acceptance of Lowell's charts necessarily involves acceptance of his whole theory.

However, few astronomers nowadays do accept Lowell's charts. Even when first published, they were challenged by other equally skilled observers who could see absolutely no trace of the canal network. E. E. Barnard, using equipment superior to Lowell's, could see only indications of broad, diffuse streaks where Lowell drew sharp lines, and others were even less successful.

There never was, and never has been, any suggestion that Lowell

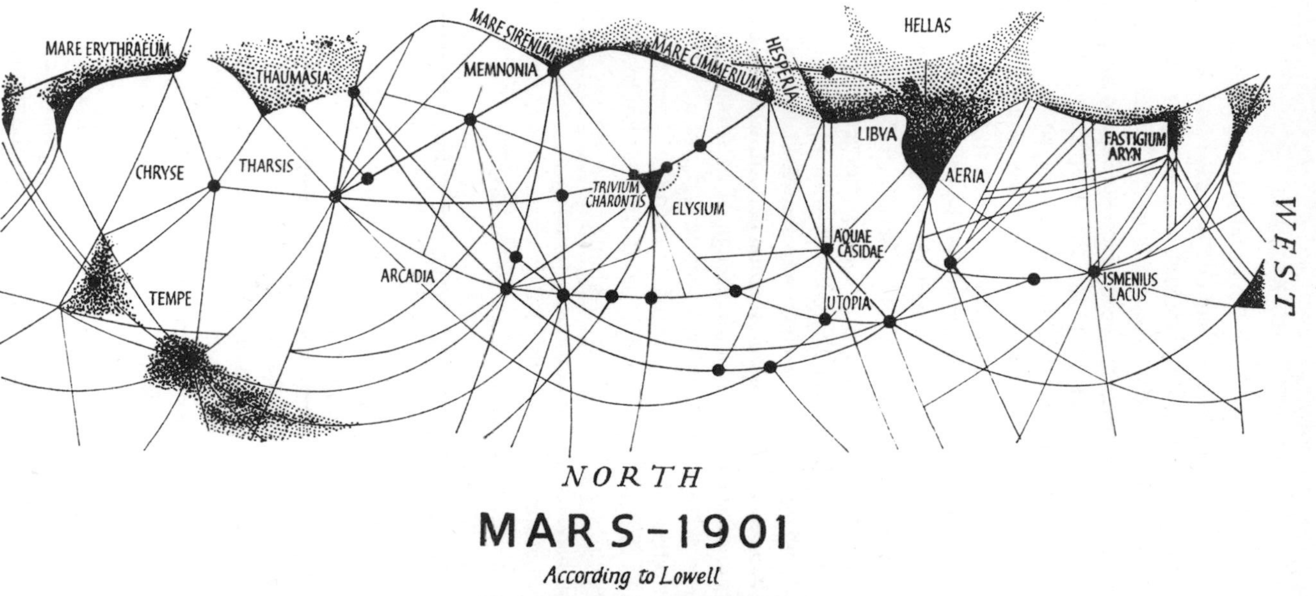

FIG. 29. Lowell's chart of Mars

was deliberately exaggerating the canal system. Such an idea is quite absurd. Yet unfortunately there are a great many disquieting facts. For one thing, Lowell drew linear streaks not only on Mars, but also on Mercury, Venus, and the satellites of Jupiter. Admittedly he stressed that the streaks in these cases were quite different from the canals of Mars, but even so his charts of Venus can only be described as fantastic. The features which he showed simply do not exist, and he was also mistaken about the straight lines which he drew on Mercury. If he were entirely wrong in two cases, it is logical to assume that he was also wrong in the third.

A possible explanation is that the human eye tends to join up disconnected spots and streaks into hard lines. In 1902 an interesting test was conducted by the English astronomer E. W. Maunder. A drawing of Mars, without canals but with indistinct shadings and roughly aligned dusky patches, was shown at a distance to a class of boys from the Greenwich Hospital School, who were told to copy it. None of them had any knowledge of astronomy, but when the drawings were collected it was seen that many of the boys had put in thin, straight 'canals'. Lowell dismissed the experiment contemptuously as the 'small boy theory', but there is no doubt that the human eye becomes unreliable when straining to see details at the very limit of visibility.

Photography is of no help. It is claimed that the canals can be detected only at moments of perfect seeing, and the slightest tremor in the Earth's atmosphere will blot them out, which renders all time-exposures of more than a second's duration useless for the purpose.

Lowell's final book, *Mars and its Canals*, was published in 1908, and caused a tremendous amount of argument. One school of thought held that Lowell's charts were accurate, and conclusive as to the existence of intelligent life on Mars; other astronomers stated baldly that the canals were illusory, and had no real existence. Some observers claimed that they could see the network on any favourable night; others could see no trace of it. Such was the position in 1916, when Lowell himself died.

Even today the position is not entirely clear, but the problem is a different one. We can certainly reject the thin, artificial-looking canals drawn by Lowell, as they have never been seen by any other observer using comparable equipment – and the numerous drawings made by observers using small telescopes cannot be relied on.[1] What we have to decide is whether the canals exist in any form whatsoever.

Some of the features – such as the Nepenthes-Thoth, which joins the famous Syrtis Major – are easy enough, but take the form of broad patches, and are not in the least canal-like. Observations of narrow lines are much less conclusive, though it is important to note that in 1956 R. S. Richardson, using the Mount Wilson 60-inch reflector, saw a number of canals as 'bluish veins'.

E. M. Antoniadi, who studied Mars intensively with the Meudon 33-inch refractor, was violently opposed to Lowell's theories, and in 1930 he wrote that 'no-one has ever seen a true canal on Mars. The rectilinear canals, single or double, do not exist . . . though they have a basis of reality, since all are situated either on spotted irregular tracks or rugged grey borders.' This theme has been followed up in recent years by A. Dollfus, at the Pic du Midi. Dollfus states that under normal conditions, canals are sometimes visible with the 24-inch Pic refractor, but when seeing conditions become really good the regularity of the canals disappears, to be replaced by disconnected spots and streaks.

Personal bias is bound to enter into the canal argument, however much one may wish to eliminate it, and so it may not be irrelevant for me to give some of my own views on the matter.

I began observing Mars as long ago as 1935, but it was not until 1948 that I was able to make regular use of an adequate telescope. I recorded a few streaky features which I refused to regard as canals, but even so I tended to exaggerate their narrowness whenever I tried to draw them. In 1950 I repeated Maunder's 'small boy' experiment, and showed a disk drawing of the same sort to the pupils of a large preparatory school in Kent. The boys' ages ranged between nine and fourteen, and all had had lessons in art, though of course not all of them had any artistic ability. Out of 58 drawings, three showed canals and the rest did not; it may or may not be significant that out of the exceptional three, two of the boys concerned were notoriously inartistic and the third short-sighted. My results do not, therefore, confirm Maunder's, and I am very doubtful of the value of any experiments of this sort.

[1] It is always tempting to draw elusive features as being smaller than they really are, and I have seen drawings of Mars showing canals which are impossibly narrow.

During the favourable oppositions of 1958 and 1960–1 I was able to use some very large telescopes to study Mars, and also carried out a series of observations with my own 12½-inch reflector. I can only say that I have yet to see anything which looks in the least like a Lowell-type canal, but, as Antoniadi pointed out, some of them have a basis of reality, and streaky patches exist here and there.

The 'canals', using the term in its widest sense, seem on the whole to be natural features, presumably made up of the same material as that which composes the dark areas. Various far-fetched explanations have been put forward recently: for instance E. J. Öpik believes that Mars has suffered severe meteoric bombardment and has a crack-riddled surface, so that a canal takes the form of a deep valley in and round which vegetation may flourish. Yet when seen under good conditions, the Martian surface shows no features which may be suitably explained in any such way.

Though there seems virtually no chance that advanced creatures live on Mars, it is by no means absurd to suggest that men from our own world will be able to go there before many decades have passed by. If the Moon is reached well before A.D. 2000, as is quite possible, the first Martian voyage should take place before A.D. 2100. Of course the difficulties will be much greater, since the journey will take many months instead of less than forty-eight hours; and since the pioneers will have to spend some time on Mars before the return journey can be begun, it will be necessary to establish some kind of headquarters on the planet itself. Much has been written about the future 'Martian Base', but we cannot yet be certain what it will be like. Our best hope of finding out more about surface conditions on Mars lies in the unmanned probe-rockets now in an advanced planning stage.

All things considered, Mars is probably the most fascinating of the planets. It is basically similar to the Earth; it is not hopelessly cold; it has atmosphere and moisture; and almost certainly it supports living organisms, so that even if it has long since passed the prime of life it is still very far from being a dead world.

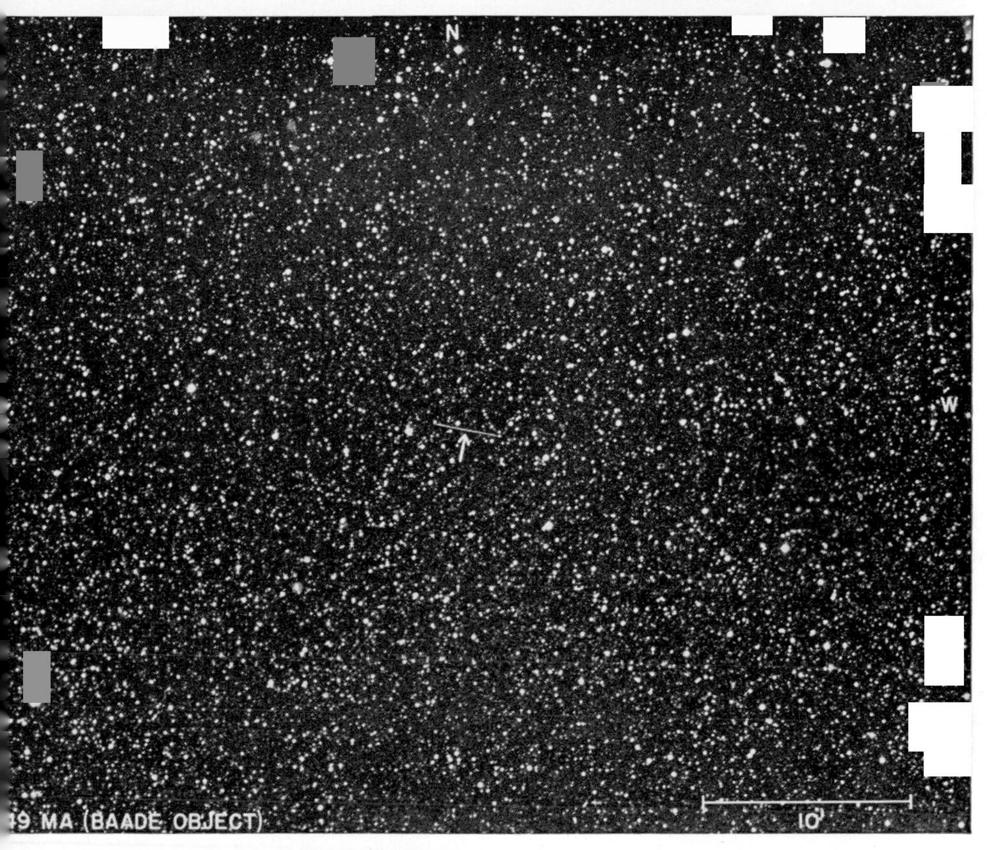

Trail of Icarus. The asteroid trail, near the centre of the photograph, is indicated by an arrow. (48-inch Schmidt photograph, Mount Wilson and Palomar Observatories)

XII Jupiter, in blue light, showing the Great Red Spot. Satellite Ganymede and shadow (above) (1952 Oct 23, 23 h. 41 m., photograph, Mount Wilson and Palomar Observatories). Taken with the 200-inch Hale Reflector

Chapter 10

The Minor Planets

MARS IS THE OUTERMOST of the four so-called 'terrestrial' planets. Beyond it there is a 350-million-mile gap before we come to Jupiter, first of the giants. This gap in the Solar System was noticed in comparatively early times. Kepler, the great mathematician who drew up the three famous laws of planetary motion, suspected that the solar family must be incomplete, and went so far as to write: 'Between Mars and Jupiter I put a planet.'

It was clear that even if such a planet existed, it could not be large. Even a world the size of the Moon would be readily visible without a telescope at all. But the problem of the missing planet was brought into prominence in 1772 by a German astronomer named Johann Bode, who drew attention to a curious numerical relationship which had been discovered some years earlier by another German, Titius of Wittenberg. Rather unfairly, perhaps, it is always known as Bode's Law, and is interesting enough to give in full.

Take the numbers 0, 3, 6, 12, 24, 48, 96, 192, and 384, each of which (after 3) is double its predecessors. Now add 4 to each, giving: 4, 7, 10, 16, 28, 52, 100, 196, 388. Taking the Earth's distance from the Sun as 10, this series of numbers gives us the distances of the remaining planets, to scale, with remarkable accuracy. The following table will make this clear:

Planet	Distance by Bode's Law	Actual distance
Mercury	4	3·9
Venus	7	7·2
The Earth	10	10·0
Mars	16	15·2
—	28	—
Jupiter	52	52·0
Saturn	100	95·4
Uranus	196	191·8
Neptune	—	300·7
Pluto	388	394·6

The three outer planets, Uranus, Neptune, and Pluto, were not known when Titius worked out the relationship; but when Uranus was discovered, in 1781, it was found to fit excellently into the general scheme. Neptune, admittedly, is a 'problem child'. According to Bode's Law it ought not to be there, and the last figure (388) corresponds well enough to the actual mean distance of Pluto. Yet at the time of its discovery the Law seemed to be very precise – except for the missing planet corresponding to figure 28.

In 1800 six astronomers assembled at the little German town of Lilienthal, determined to make a serious effort to track down the missing planet. These 'celestial police', as they were named, elected the hard-working Schröter as their president, with the Baron von Zach as secretary. Between them they worked out a scheme according to which each observer would be responsible for one particular part of the ecliptic, where the planet, if it existed at all, would probably be found.

Naturally, a plan of this sort takes some time to bring into working order, and before Schröter's 'police' were fully organized they had been forestalled. Piazzi, director of the Sicilian observatory of Palermo, was compiling a star catalogue, and on 1801 January 1 – the first day of the new century – he picked up a starlike object which behaved in a most unstarlike manner. It moved appreciably from night to night. Piazzi at first took it for a tail-less comet, but he went so far as to write to von Zach; evidently he had his suspicions. By the time that von Zach received the letter, the moving body had been lost in the rays of the Sun.

Fortunately Piazzi had made enough observations to enable an orbit to be worked out. It was soon clear that the object was not a comet at all, but a planet. It was re-detected exactly a year after its original discovery, and Piazzi named it Ceres in honour of the patron goddess of Sicily. It was found to have a distance of 27·7 on the Bode scale, which corresponded most satisfactorily with the predicted 28. The Solar System was complete.

Yet Ceres turned out to be a miniature world less than 500 miles in diameter, and seemed hardly worthy to be ranked with the other planets. Significantly, the 'celestial police' continued their efforts, and it came as no real surprise when one of the observers, H. Olbers, picked up a second small planet in March 1802. Pallas, as it was named, was so like Ceres in size and orbit that Olbers suggested that

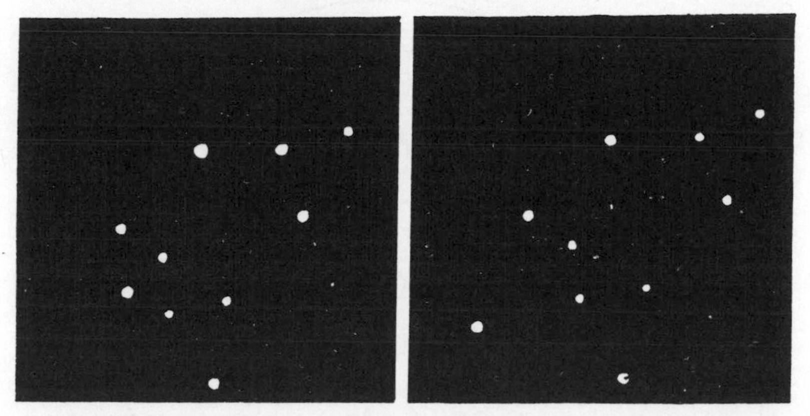

FIG. 30. Movement of Ceres: A 1921 Jan. 6; B 1921 Jan. 10 (3-inch refractor, × 80; H. P. Wilkins)

the two had been formed from one larger body which had met with disaster. The idea was attractive; if there were two fragments, there might be others – and two more planets came to light within the next five years. Juno was discovered by Karl Harding in 1804, and Vesta by Olbers in 1807.

Juno and Vesta resembled the two senior members of the group, and the four became generally known as the Minor Planets or 'asteroids'. No more seemed to be forthcoming, and the 'celestial police' disbanded in 1815. Schröter himself died in the following year.

Nothing more was done until 1830, when a Prussian amateur named Hencke took up the problem and began a systematic search for new asteroids. Alone and unaided, he worked away for fifteen years, and at last had his reward – a fifth minor planet, now named Astræa, circling the Sun at a distance slightly greater than Vesta's, slightly less than Juno's. However, Astræa was considerably fainter than the first four, and its estimated diameter is only just over 100 miles.

Even the enthusiastic Hencke would have been surprised to learn that his discovery was a mere prelude to thousands more. He himself found another asteroid, Hebe, in 1847; in the same year Hind, in London, discovered Iris and Flora; 1848 and 1849 yielded one asteroid each, but since then every year has produced its quota. By 1870 the total number of known asteroids was 109, and twenty

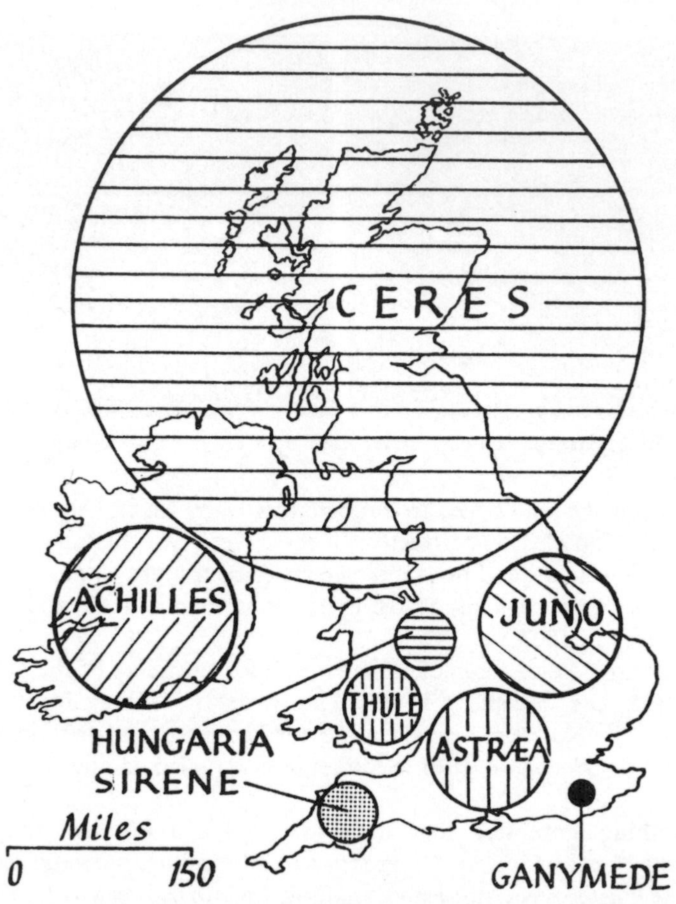

FIG. 31. Sizes of asteroids, compared with England, Scotland, Ireland and Wales

years later this had grown to 300. Then, in 1891, Max Wolf of Heidelberg introduced a new method which led to a startling increase.

Wolf's method was a photographic one. If a camera is adjusted to follow the ordinary stars in their movement across the sky, an asteroid will show up as a streak across the plate – because an asteroid moves among the stars sufficiently quickly for its shift to be detectable with a time-exposure of only an hour or two. If I set my camera to photograph a garden, and then walk in front of the lens during a time-exposure, I will appear as a blur, because of my movement. The asteroid will not blur, because it is a hard, sharp point of light, but its movement will certainly betray it.

The Wolf method was almost embarrassingly successful, and the numbers of known asteroids increased by leaps and bounds. Wolf was personally responsible for adding over a hundred, and by the year 1961 there were 1,627 asteroids with properly worked-out orbits. At least a thousand more had been found on photographic plates without having been under observation for long enough to have their paths computed.

It cannot be said that the asteroids proved to be popular members of the Solar System. Plates exposed for quite different reasons were often found to be swarming with short tracks, and the irritating little planets complicated star-counts and similar work to such an extent that German astronomers, who nobly established a computing centre to try to keep pace with them,[1] started referring to the 'Kleineplanetenplage' (minor planet pest). One American observer went so far as to nickname them 'vermin of the skies'.

Another difficulty was to find names for them. The early asteroids were given dignified mythological names such as Psyche, Thetis, Proserpine, and Circe; but as time went on, and the numbers grew and grew, the supply of mythological names began to give out. Many of the later names are odd, to say the least of it. For instance, No. 724 is named Hapag, the initials of a German navigation line, the Hamburg Amerika Paketfahrt Aktien Gesellschaft, while No. 694 is Ekard, the word 'Drake' spelled backwards – it was christened by two members of Drake University in America!

The normal asteroids are, perhaps, the least notable of the members of the Solar System. Few are as much as 100 miles across, and all are devoid of atmosphere, so that they cannot support life. The smaller bodies are mere pieces of matter, probably not even approximately spherical. One or two have unusual paths; that of Pallas has an inclination of 34° 48′, and No. 279, Thule, is unusually remote, since it circles the Sun at an average distance of almost 400 million miles as against the 257 million miles of Ceres. Only one, Vesta, is ever bright enough to be seen without a telescope – and then only if one knows just where to look for it.

Towards the end of the last century, it was noticed that the asteroids

[1] Nowadays this work is carried out at Cincinnati, in the United States, from which regular Minor Planet Circulars are issued.

tend to fall into groups. This effect is quite genuine, and is due to the tremendous disturbing influence of the giant planet Jupiter. However, all the asteroids seemed to keep strictly to the gap between the orbits of Jupiter and Mars, and no one was prepared for the peculiar behaviour of No. 433, Eros, which was discovered in 1898 by Witt at Berlin.

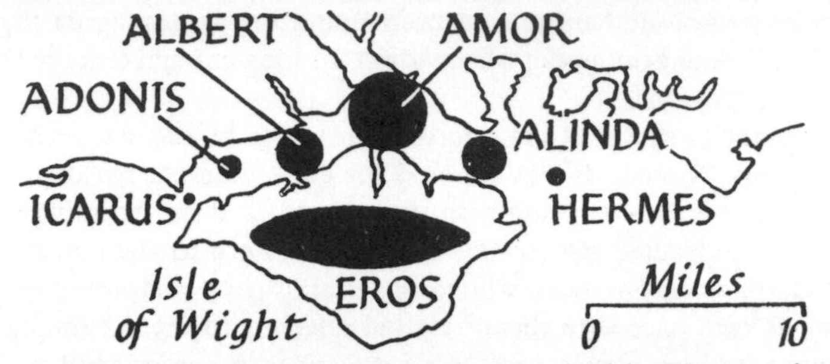

FIG. 32. Sizes of asteroids, compared with the Isle of Wight. The exact size and shape of Eros is uncertain

Eros is one of the smaller members of the asteroid swarm, and is never a conspicuous object. Its oddity lies in the fact that it comes well inside the main group. Its orbit is of some eccentricity, so that the aphelion point lies well beyond Mars, but at perihelion it moves much closer to the Sun; consequently it can at times approach the Earth, and its minimum distance from us is only 14,000,000 miles. Close approaches are rare, and the next is not due until 1975; but in 1931 Eros passed within 17,000,000 miles of the Earth, and was not difficult to see with a moderate telescope.

When at its nearest, Eros is so close to us that its distance can be measured very accurately, and this gives us a key to the whole scale of the Solar System – in particular, to the distance of the Earth from the Sun. Hundreds of photographic measurements of it made in 1931 enabled H. Spencer Jones to arrive at the figure of 93,003,000 miles for the length of the 'astronomical unit' or Earth–Sun distance. This was the most reliable value calculated up to that time, and was not bettered until very recently – which shows that Eros at least has its uses, and compensates in some measure for its irritating fellows.[1]

[1] It is easy to see why some astronomers regard the asteroids with disfavour. Some years ago S. B. Nicolson was using the 100-inch Mount Wilson reflector to search for faint new satellites of Jupiter. Altogether his photographic plates recorded 32 unexpected asteroids, all of which had to be eliminated as possible Jovian moons, and which wasted an incredible amount of time.

Eros is interesting in itself as well as in its movements. In 1931 it was found that the light showed variations in an average period of about five hours. Since no planet or asteroid has any light of its own, the only explanation was that Eros must be irregular in shape; this was confirmed by van den Bos, who saw the asteroid oval at times. It has been calculated that Eros is 15 miles long and about 4 wide, so that it does indeed resemble a piece of cosmic débris.

For some time Eros was thought to be unique, but in 1911 Palisa, at Vienna, picked up a tiny body which can approach the Earth to within 20,000,000 miles, though its orbit is so eccentric that its aphelion distance is almost as great as that of remote Thule. It was numbered 719, and was named Albert. Unfortunately it is only about 3 miles in diameter, and after its brief visit in 1911 it vanished into the distance; so far it has not been re-discovered. A minute body such as Albert is susceptible to even the slightest perturbations, and recovery is bound to be largely a matter of luck. We simply cannot work out its orbit accurately enough to tell just when it will reappear, unless a long series of observations is obtained.

No. 887, Alinda, discovered by Wolf in 1918, and No. 1036, Ganymede,[1] found by W. Baade in 1924, are other asteroids with orbits of the Albert type; but all these, Eros included, were outdone by Amor and Apollo, the two 'earth-grazers' of 1932.

No. 1221, Amor, discovered by the Belgian astronomer Delporte, is a full 5 miles across, so that it is about equal to Deimos – the second satellite of Mars – and considerably larger than Albert. It came within 10,000,000 miles of the Earth, and was under observation for long enough to enable the mathematicians to work out a really good orbit. Amor has a period of 975 days, and after it had been twice round the Sun unseen it was picked up again in 1940.

However, Amor's reign as a record-holder was brief. Apollo, discovered by Reinmuth at Heidelberg later in 1932, approached the Earth to within 7,000,000 miles. At perihelion it is a mere 59,000,000 miles from the Sun – closer in than the Earth or Venus – and so it can play some strange tricks. Like Mars and the outer planets, it is best seen at opposition; but it can also pass through inferior conjunction, and it can even transit the Sun's disk, though it is so small

[1] This is a bad choice of name, as the third satellite of Jupiter is also called Ganymede. No. 1036 is rather larger than other members of its group, and seems to be about 20 miles in diameter.

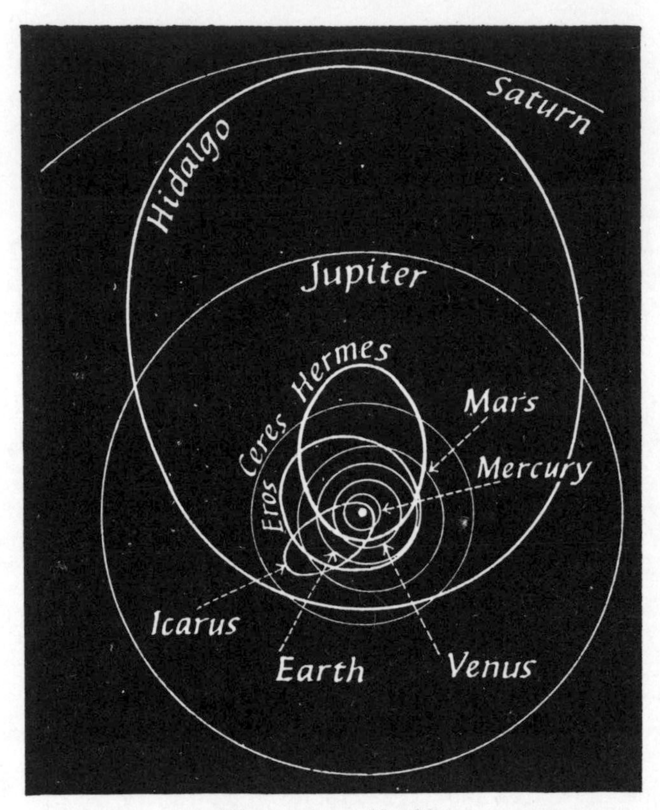

FIG. 33. Asteroid orbits

that it could not possibly be observed during transit. Unhappily Apollo, like Albert, has been lost, and today we do not know where it is.

Adonis, found by Delporte in 1936, veered past us at only 1,300,000 miles, and at perihelion approaches the orbit of Mercury, but it also has been lost. In 1937 Reinmuth discovered an even more interesting earth-grazer, subsequently named Hermes. Even smaller than Adonis, with an estimated diameter of only a mile, it passed by at a distance of only 485,000 miles, barely double that of the Moon. It is possible for it to come still closer, actually passing between the Earth and Moon.

Needless to say, astronomers were not in the least alarmed by this celestial visitor. Hermes may have been very close in the astronomical sense, but there was no danger of a collision; in fact, the chances of our being hit by an earth-grazer are millions to one against. If we reduce the Earth in scale to a 12-inch globe, Hermes may be compared with a speck of dust passing several feet away.

It is true, of course, that if a collision really did take place, the damage would be widespread. In 1908 a meteorite with a diameter of perhaps a quarter of a mile hit Siberia, devastating an area of hundreds of square miles – and there is no difference, except in name, between a large meteorite and a small asteroid.[1] When the Hermes story was made known, in January 1938, the Press seized upon it with avidity, and the headlines of national papers on January 10 were highly sensational. 'World Disaster Missed by Five Hours', was one example; 'Scientists Watch a Planet Hurtling Earthward.' However, Hermes, interesting though it is, was certainly no threat. At the moment it is lost, but it may be re-discovered one day.

Mars, closer to the main swarm than we are, also has its visitors. No. 1009, Sirene, can pass within 5,000,000 miles of the Red Planet, and doubtless there are small asteroids which go even closer in.

For many years Thule was thought to be the outermost member of the asteroid group, but in 1906 Max Wolf, at Heidelberg, detected No. 588, Achilles, which was obviously more remote. In fact, it appeared to move in almost the same orbit as Jupiter. Further investigations showed that this was indeed the case.

As long before as 1772, the famous mathematician Lagrange had called attention to the special 'problem of three bodies' which arises when a massive planet and a tiny asteroid move round the Sun in the same plane, in circular orbits and with equal periods. Lagrange found that in such a case, if the bodies are 60 degrees apart they will always remain 60 degrees apart. At that time the problem was regarded as of theoretical interest only, but Achilles provided a practical example. Moreover, it was not the only one. Other similar asteroids were found, and were given names of combatants in the war between Greece and Troy, so that nowadays these remote asteroids are known collectively as the Trojans.

[1] As we have seen, a recent Russian theory suggests that the Siberian object may have been the nucleus of a small comet, but the principles involved are just the same.

Sixteen Trojans have been discovered, but two have been lost again because they were not observed for long enough to have reliable orbits worked out. The remaining fourteen are split into two groups on opposite sides of Jupiter. Sixty degrees ahead of Jupiter lie 1404 Ajax, 659 Nestor, 1647 Menelaus, 624 Hector, 911 Agamemnon, 1143 Odysseus, 1437 Diomedes, 588 Achilles, and 1583 Antilochus; sixty degrees behind come 1173 Anchises, 1208 Troilus, 617 Patroclus, 1172 Æneas, and 884 Priamus.

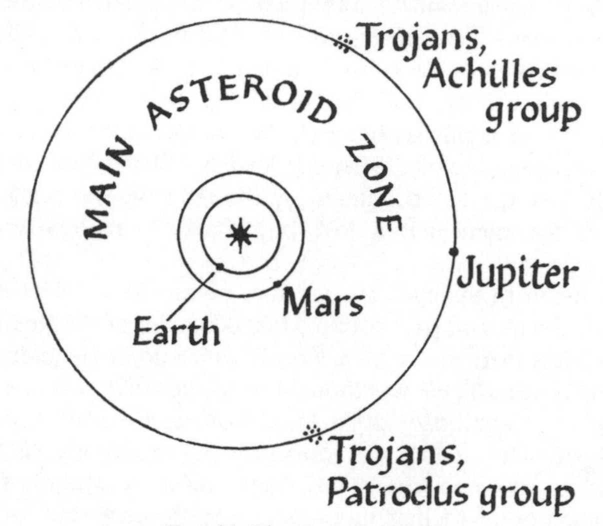

FIG. 34. The Trojan asteroids

The Trojans do not, of course, keep strictly 60 degrees ahead of or behind Jupiter, because we are dealing with elliptical orbits, and moreover there are various other perturbations to be taken into account – particularly those due to Saturn. Diomedes, for instance, may go as far as 40 degrees beyond the 60-degree point on the side away from Jupiter, and 24 degrees from it on the side towards Jupiter. All the members of the group are faint: the largest, Hector, is around 50 miles in diameter, while Menelaus is probably no more than a dozen miles across. There can be no doubt that other Trojans exist, in addition to the two which have been found and then lost again.

Jupiter has seven small satellites which move at great distances from the planet, and it has been suggested that these are nothing more than captured Trojans. On the other hand, it is equally possible that the Trojans themselves are ex-satellites of Jupiter which somehow 'got away'. So far we do not have enough information to decide one way or the other.

It was thought that the Trojans marked the extreme outer limit of the asteroid swarm, but this did not prove to be so. Hidalgo, discovered by Baade in 1920, is not a Trojan, but has a most extraordinary orbit which carries it from inside the main group almost as far as Saturn. Its period is fourteen years, and its path is so eccentric that it moves more in the manner of a comet than an asteroid. In fact, its nature was for some time suspect. It was carefully photographed with the 100-inch reflector at Mount Wilson, but always showed up as a sharp point of light, devoid of any trace of the fuzziness which betrays a comet. Rather reluctantly, we are bound to include Hidalgo in the asteroid family, though with the inner feeling that it is something of a black sheep!

The movements of the more normal asteroids are not without interest. As we have seen, the minor planets tend to fall into well-defined groups, and five of these groups contain large numbers of asteroids whose orbits are so alike that they seem probably to have had a common origin. This brings us back to Olbers' theory of a disrupted planet which originally circled the Sun between Mars and Jupiter.

For many years this idea was in disfavour, but now the pendulum seems to be swinging back to it. According to the Dutch astronomer Oort, the original planet exploded; the fragments thrown into nearly circular orbits provided the asteroids and meteorites, while those with more elliptical orbits were so violently perturbed by Jupiter and the other giant planets that some were driven out of the Solar System altogether, while the remainder formed an outer cloud of comets. It has also been suggested that there were two or more original planets, which broke up by collision. However, there is no general agreement, and it may well be that the asteroids (and meteorites) never formed one larger body.

The low escape velocities of the asteroids mean that they cannot hold on to any sort of atmosphere. This applies even to Ceres, which is much the largest of the swarm. Consequently, any form of life as we know it is totally out of the question.

Before leaving these miniature worlds, something should be said about perhaps the most remarkable of all – Icarus, discovered by Baade in June 1949.

When discovered it was about 8,000,000 miles away, and as it can never come closer to us than about 4,000,000 miles it is not an earth-grazer in the sense that Adonis and Hermes are. Yet it is unique inasmuch that at perihelion it passes within 20,000,000 miles of the Sun, much closer than Mercury. At aphelion it recedes to a distance of 183,000,000 miles, well beyond Mars. In addition to being very eccentric, the orbit is also sharply inclined, so that it never actually intersects that of the Earth.

Icarus, a tiny world only a mile or so across, was named after the youth who is said to have escaped from Crete with the aid of artificial wings, but who flew so close to the Sun that the wax of his wings melted and he plunged to his death in the sea. At its hottest, it must be so fiercely warmed that its surface glows a dull red; six months later, when near aphelion, the temperature is extremely low. All things considered, it must be regarded as the most uncomfortable body in the whole Solar System.

It has often been suggested that in the far future, some of the larger and more conventional asteroids may be pressed into service as space-stations. This sounds very much like pure science fiction, and is likely to remain so; it is certainly impossible to tow an asteroid into a convenient path, as has been recommended from time to time! In any case, Icarus, scorched and frozen during each 400-day revolution round the Sun, will be left severely alone.

To the ordinary observer, the asteroids are of little interest; they show no measurable disks, and even when found they seem hardly worth the trouble spent on the search. Yet they are not without their value; and the strange orbits of Eros, Achilles, Hidalgo, Icarus, and their kind show us that it is unjust to dismiss all the minor planets as mere 'vermin of the skies'.

Chapter 11

Jupiter

FAR BEYOND THE MAIN asteroid swarm, nearly 500 million miles from the Sun, circles mighty Jupiter, giant of the Solar System. The ancients named it after the King of the Gods, and the name is indeed appropriate, since Jupiter is more than twice as massive as all the other planets put together. Its globe could contain over thirteen hundred bodies the size of the Earth.

Even though it is so remote, Jupiter appears as a splendid object in our skies. It is brighter than any other planet apart from Venus and (very occasionally) Mars; at times it may even cast a shadow. Its orbital velocity is less than half that of the Earth, so that it comes to opposition every year; its *synodic period*, or average interval between successive oppositions, is 399 days. The revolution period amounts to nearly 12 years.

Jupiter's equatorial diameter is 88,700 miles, over eleven times that of the Earth, but even a small telescope will show that the disk is flattened, so that the diameter as measured through the poles is only 83,800 miles. There is no mystery about this. Although Jupiter is the largest planet in the Solar System, it has the shortest axial

FIG. 35. Comparative sizes of Jupiter and the Earth

rotation period – less than 10 hours – and so is spinning at a tremendous rate; particles at the equator are whirling round at no less than 28,000 m.p.h. Centrifugal force is so strong in the equatorial zone that it produces a noticeable bulge. There is a similar effect in the case of the Earth, but for our own world the difference between the equatorial and polar diameters amounts to less than 30 miles, as against 5,000 miles for Jupiter.

This pronounced flattening indicates that Jupiter cannot be 'solid' in the sense that the four inner planets are. Telescopic observation leads us to the same conclusion. As with Venus, we look not at a solid surface with mountains, plateaux, and deserts, but upon a sea of clouds – shifting and changing unceasingly. However, there is no real comparison with Venus, and Jupiter is a world of completely different type. Instead of a relatively shallow atmosphere surrounding a solid globe, Jupiter has a mantle which must be extremely deep.

In a way, it is misleading to speak of the outer cloud-layers of Jupiter as making up an 'atmosphere'. More properly, they are part of the body of the planet, and the mean density of the globe is surprisingly low – only 1·3 times greater than that of water. Though Jupiter has a tremendous gravitational pull, it is only 317 times as massive as the Earth, and it would take over a thousand Jupiters to make one body as massive as the Sun.

The surface temperature never rises much above —200 degrees Fahrenheit. This, together with the gaseous nature of the outer layers, is enough to rule out Jupiter as an abode of life; we cannot picture any organisms which could survive there. Moreover, the Jovian gas itself has proved to be decidedly unwelcoming.

For analyzing Jupiter's clouds, the essential instrument is of course the spectroscope. As long ago as 1872 some prominent dark lines were found in the spectrum of Jupiter, and Lowell, in 1907, managed to take excellent photographs of them. At that time it was thought that Jupiter and the other giant planets were hot and shone partly by their own light, so that they were intermediate in type between planets and stars. This intriguing idea had to be given up when it was found that the surface temperatures were very low; in any case, modern theories have shown that nothing of the sort would be possible. Meanwhile, the dark lines in the spectrum needed explaining.

The problem was solved by R. Wildt, a German astronomer who

has spent many years in the United States. Wildt showed that the gases responsible for the bands were ammonia and methane, both of which are compounds of hydrogen.[1] Consequently, many people still think that the outer layers of Jupiter are made up chiefly of ammonia and methane, with only small quantities of other substances.

Yet this is not so. There can be little doubt that the bulk of the gas is ordinary hydrogen, together with a considerable amount of helium. Methane and ammonia are present, and Wildt's work on the spectrum has been fully confirmed, but hydrogen is the main constituent. The reason is that Jupiter has the very high escape velocity

FIG. 36. Wildt's model of Jupiter

of 37 miles per second, and its original hydrogen could not leak away into space, as the Earth's did.

Once these basic facts had been established, the next step was to decide what Jupiter must be like lower down. Here the spectroscope could give no more help than the simple telescope, and observers had to give way to theorists. Wildt himself produced a model which became widely accepted: he suggested that Jupiter has a rocky, metallic core 37,000 miles in diameter overlaid by an ice layer 17,000 miles thick, which is in turn overlaid by the hydrogen-rich atmosphere.

[1] Ammonia is made up of hydrogen and nitrogen (chemical formula NH_3); methane, better known by its common name of marsh gas, is carbon and hydrogen (CH_4). Under terrestrial conditions – that is to say, mixed with oxygen – methane is dangerously explosive. Miners dread it, and call it 'fire-damp'.

If Wildt's model is correct, conditions at the bottom of the atmosphere – 8,000 miles below the visible surface – will be strange indeed. The high pressure will make the material behave in the manner of a solid, though it will still be 'gaseous' in the technical sense.

More recently, Wildt's theory has been challenged by W. Ramsey, formerly of the University of Manchester. According to Ramsey, Jupiter is composed mainly of hydrogen all the way to its centre, but most of the hydrogen is in a state quite unfamiliar to us. Since Ramsey's hypothesis has met with strong support, it is worth describing in slightly more detail.

We begin, as before, with an outer atmosphere made up of hydrogen, together with hydrogen compounds such as ammonia and methane as well as some helium. Below the visible surface the pressure mounts rapidly, and the density of the hydrogen increases, so that it takes on the characteristics of a solid. At a depth of 2,000 miles, the pressure is 200,000 times that of the Earth's atmosphere at sea-level, and the solid hydrogen has a density of one-third that of water.

At 5,000 miles there is a sudden change. The pressure has grown to 800,000 atmospheres, and instead of being a highly compressed solid the hydrogen starts to behave like a metal. Metallic hydrogen is more readily compressible than more ordinary solid hydrogen, and at the centre of the planet the density is 3·7 times that of water – much the same as that of a diamond.

Now let us sum up Ramsey's model for Jupiter. There is a core of metallic hydrogen 76,000 miles in diameter, accounting for over 90 per cent. of the total mass of the planet. Above this comes a shell of solid hydrogen 5,000 miles deep, and on the very outside there is a comparatively shallow 'atmosphere' ending in the visible surface which we can examine with our telescopes.

Which of these models is correct – or are they both wrong? So far we cannot tell, and neither can we hope that rocket probes will be able to clear the matter up in the foreseeable future, since Jupiter is so remote that for the present it is well beyond the range even of small unmanned vehicles. All we can say definitely is that Jupiter and the other giants must be built upon the same pattern, and that this pattern is utterly different from that of Earth.

Jupiter is a fascinating object even in a small telescope. There is

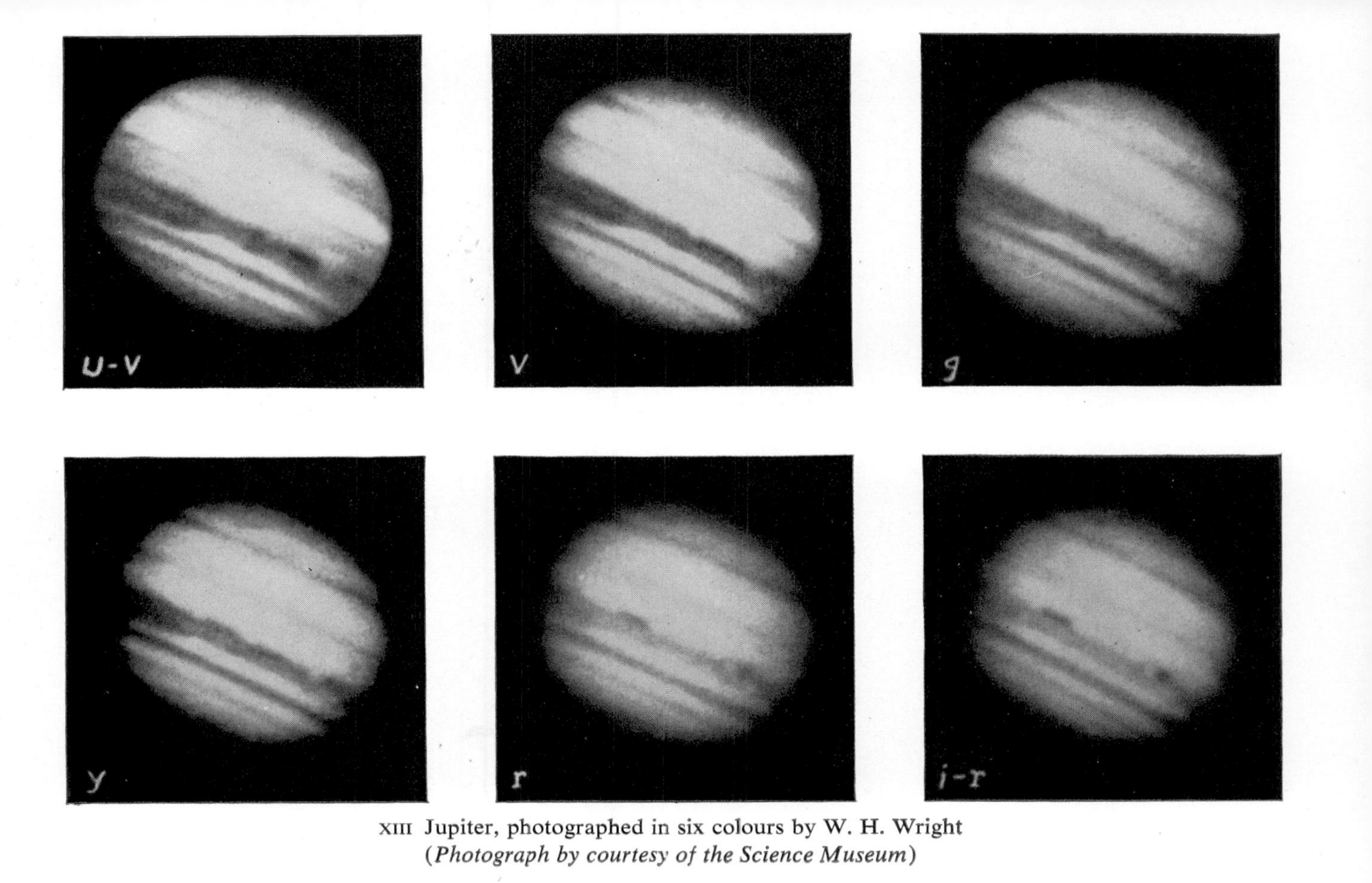

XIII Jupiter, photographed in six colours by W. H. Wright
(*Photograph by courtesy of the Science Museum*)

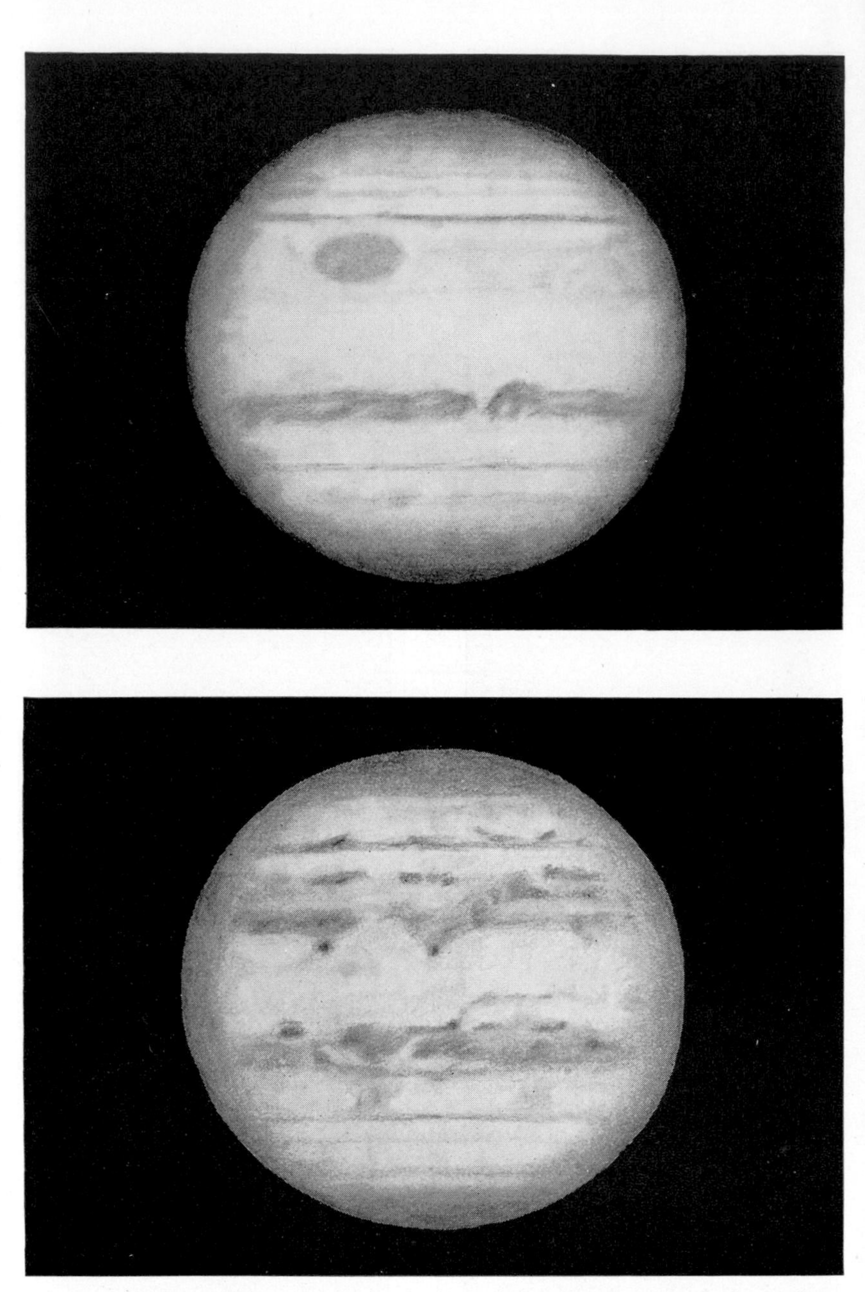

XIV Jupiter. Contrasting activity in the lateral cloud systems above the surface. (Drawings by L. F. Ball)

Top. 1957 March 20. 20 hours. 10 inch × 260.
Bottom. 1934 April 14. 23½ hours. 10 inch × 300.

abundant detail to be seen, and this detail is always changing, so that we can never tell just what is going to happen next.

The most prominent markings on the yellowish, flattened disk are the so-called cloud belts. There are several of them, running straight across the planet, and all drawings and photographs show them. At a casual glance they appear as dark, regular lines, but closer examination shows that they are far from regular. They reveal fine structure, with brighter and fainter portions, knots, divisions, spots, and notches.

The generally accepted nomenclature for the main features of

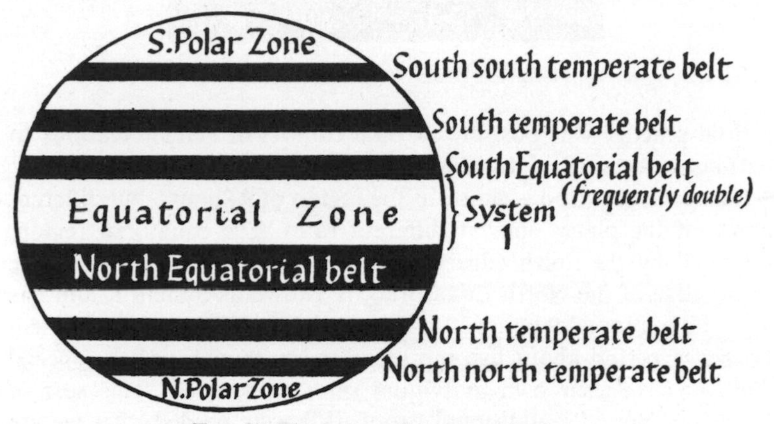

FIG. 37. The belts and zones of Jupiter

Jupiter is given in the diagram. Of the belts, the North Equatorial is generally the most conspicuous, followed by the South Equatorial, South Temperate, and North Temperate. Yet variations are always going on. In 1959, for instance, the South Equatorial was more prominent than the South Temperate, but conditions were reversed in 1960, while in 1958 the South Equatorial had been very obscure.

Details on the disk often last for weeks or months, and it is therefore an easy matter to find out the rotation period. Amateurs have done valuable work here, mainly by the method of transits. As Jupiter spins, the markings seem to be carried across the disk from one side to the other, and all that has to be done is to measure the time when any particular marking reaches the central meridian of Jupiter – after which its longitude on the surface can be worked out. Two successive transits will of course yield the rotation period. With

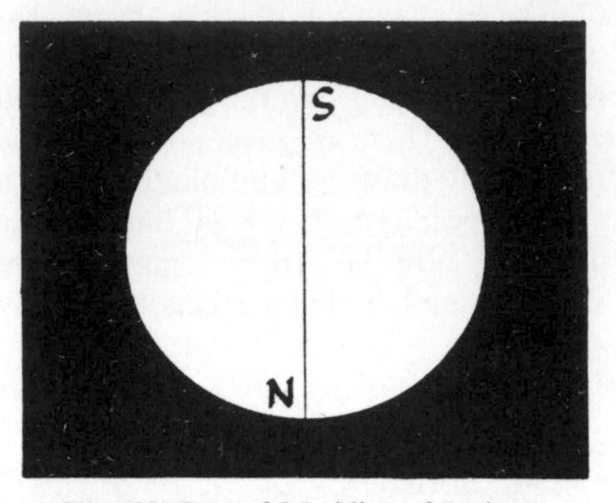

FIG. 38. Central Meridian of Jupiter

a little practice it is possible to time transits of surface features to within an accuracy of less than half a minute.

The general period is short, in the region of 9¾ hours, but different zones of the planet spin at different rates. The equatorial region, bounded by the north edge of the South Equatorial belt and the south edge of the North Equatorial, is known as System I, and has a period of around 9 hours 50 minutes; the rest of the planet (System II) has a period about five minutes longer, though various special features have their own individual rates of rotation. This sort of behaviour provides additional proof, if it were needed, that we are not dealing with a solid, rocky surface.

Spots are common on Jupiter. Most of them are relatively short-lived, but one of them, the Great Red Spot, is of particular interest because it has lasted for so long. In fact, it has persisted for so many years that it is tempting to regard it as at least a semi-permanent feature. It lies in a peculiar 'hollow' north of the South Temperate belt.

It first became really prominent in 1878, developing from a pale pink, oval object into a brick-red area 30,000 miles long by 7,000 wide – so that its surface area was equal to that of the Earth. Naturally it attracted a great deal of attention, and was traced with fair certainty on earlier drawings. Schwabe, a German observer best remembered for his discovery of the sunspot cycle, had drawn it in 1831, and indications of it have been found on a sketch made by Robert Hooke as long ago as 1664. If we accept the Hooke record, the Spot has persisted for almost 300 years, and must be something more than a mere 'cloud'.

The startling red colour did not last for more than a few years, and after 1882 the Spot began to fade, sometimes being recognizable only because of its characteristic 'hollow'. It revives at intervals – it was prominent in 1936, for instance – but at other times it vanishes completely. A few notes from my own observations may help to show the sort of thing which happens. In 1956 the Spot was extremely obscure, and generally difficult to see. In 1957 and 1958 it was once more a conspicuous feature of the disk, and its reddish hue was obvious; but all through 1959 it was utterly invisible, and even the 'hollow' was hard to find. In 1960 there were signs of a revival, but even so I only once saw the Spot itself with fair certainty. In 1961, it was again prominent.

There have been suggestions that its origin is due to a gigantic volcano which pokes out above the cloud-layer. Unfortunately for this theory, the Spot is not fixed in position; it drifts about within certain limits of longitude, and has been known to shift some 20,000 miles to either side of its mean position. It is best to admit that we are still very much in the dark concerning the true nature of the Spot; but recently a promising theory has been put forward by B. M. Peek, a British amateur who has become one of the world's leading authorities concerning Jupiter and who has written the standard work on the subject.

Peek begins by considering the well-known experiment of immersing an egg in a solution of salt and water. If the solution is densest near the bottom of the vessel, as will probably be the case, the egg will float at a level determined by its density. If anything happens to disturb the equilibrium of density distribution in the solution, the egg will rise or sink accordingly.

Suppose, then, that the Red Spot is a solid lump 'floating' in Jupiter's atmosphere? Much the same principles will apply. When the Spot is highest up, it will be at its most prominent; when at its lowest, it will be obscure or even invisible. Peek calculates that the total variation in depth need not exceed about 7 miles. He goes on to suggest that the Spot itself is composed of solid helium.

At present, this is about as far as we can go. In any case the Red Spot is unique of its kind, since all other spots on Jupiter are impermanent.

Associated with the Red Spot was a most interesting feature known as the South Tropical Disturbance, a dark area which was first recorded in 1901. It was slightly closer to the equator than the Spot, and had a shorter rotation period, so that every two or three years it caught the Spot up and passed it. While this was going on, there were marked interactions between the Disturbance and the Spot; the Disturbance tended to accelerate, and as it passed by it seemed to drag the Spot along with it for several thousands of miles. When the Disturbance had gone on its way, the Spot drifted back to its original position. However, the Disturbance has not been seen since 1941, and it may well have gone for good.

Many pages could be written about the fascinating objects seen on Jupiter's disk. Between 1930 and 1934, for instance, there were some strange spots which moved in a 'circulating' current in the South Temperate zone, and there are occasional violent upheavals in the South Equatorial belt. Moreover, remarkable phenomena are seen now and then. In early 1959 I found that the whole of System I, together with the two Equatorial Belts, showed an extraordinary yellow-orange colour, quite unlike anything I had ever seen on the planet before; between March and July this hue was recorded by many observers, and seemed to be in the nature of a high-altitude obscuration in the Jovian atmosphere. When Jupiter became observable once more in 1960, the colour had disappeared, and so far it remains a mystery. In 1961 the whole equatorial zone darkened, with evidence of great activity there.

An interesting discovery of recent years is that Jupiter is a source of radio waves. These emissions were first detected by two American workers, Burke and Franklin, and have been abundantly confirmed. It has been suggested that they are due to electrical phenomena in Jupiter's atmosphere, and may possibly be in the nature of tremendous thunderstorms. Preliminary studies indicate that the radio waves come from localized positions on the planet, mainly in the zone which contains the Red Spot – though not, apparently, from the Spot itself. The original discovery of radio emission from Jupiter was quite unexpected, and was in fact more or less accidental, but it has certainly provided radio astronomers with any number of fascinating problems.

When Galileo first turned his newly made telescope to the heavens, in 1609, he saw that Jupiter was attended by four starlike objects which soon proved to be satellites. Simon Marius, who observed them independently at about the same time, christened them Io, Europa, Ganymede, and Callisto; and though these names were not officially recognized until recently, they have now come into general use.

All four satellites can be seen with any small telescope, and there are various records of naked-eye observations of some of them, so that obviously they must be fairly large. The most recent values for their diameters are 2,310 miles for Io, 1,950 for Europa, 3,200 for Ganymede, and 3,220 for Callisto, in which case only Europa is smaller than our Moon; Ganymede and Callisto are appreciably larger than the planet Mercury, though not so massive.

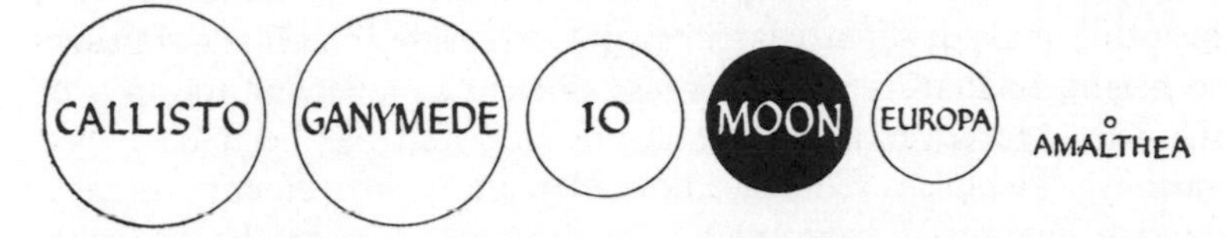

FIG. 39. Sizes of five of Jupiter's satellites, compared with the Moon

The orbits of all four 'Galileans' lie in much the same plane, and telescopically they tend to appear in a straight line. Various interesting phenomena are associated with them. They may be eclipsed by Jupiter's shadow, they may transit[1] the disk or be occulted by it, and their shadows too may be seen crossing the planet. All these phenomena are listed in yearly almanacs, and with a little practice it is not difficult to tell one satellite from another.

The four Galileans are not alike. Io and Europa have relatively high densities; that of Io is almost five times as great as that of water, and Kuiper considers that an 'excess of metals' is present, possibly covered with a surface layer of oxide smoke. Europa is smaller and less massive, but is an even better reflector of sunlight. This means that very little heat can be absorbed, and it seems that Europa must be extremely cold even by Jovian standards.

Large telescopes can show surface markings, and maps have been made of all the Galileans. Of course these maps are very rough and unreliable, but they are interesting none the less. Europa seems to be

[1] A satellite transit must not be confused with a transit observation of a feature on Jupiter's actual disk.

brightest at its poles; like its companions, it has a captured rotation, and keeps the same face towards Jupiter all the time.

Ganymede and Callisto are larger than our Moon, but much less dense, so that they seem to resemble planets in size but satellites in mass. Ganymede, the brighter, is decidedly yellow. Its density is only 2·3 times that of water, and its escape velocity is 1·7 miles per second; no trace of atmosphere has been detected, despite careful searches. Surface features are comparatively easy to see with giant telescopes, but their nature remains uncertain. It has been suggested that the globe consists of a rocky core coated with ice or even solid carbon dioxide, but we have no definite information to guide us.

Callisto, outermost of the large satellites, is in some ways the most interesting of the four, since it is strangely insubstantial. Recent measures make it slightly larger than Ganymede,[1] but it is not nearly so bright, so that its surface is less efficient at reflecting the rays of the Sun. Moreover its colour is unusual, and has been described variously as bluish, reddish, and violet. Large instruments reveal a darkish equatorial zone, and a brighter patch near the probable position of the south pole. The curiously low density has led some astronomers to suggest that Callisto is a sort of celestial snowball made up of icy, loosely-packed materials, but it may equally well have a core of light rock overlaid with a layer of ice. Owing to its low escape velocity, it is not likely to have retained any trace of atmosphere.

The transits, shadow transits, eclipses, and occultations of the four Galileans are fascinating to watch, and each satellite has its own way of behaving. During transits across the disk of Jupiter, Io and Europa are usually hard to find except when passing across a dark belt or when close to the planet's limb, whereas the less reflective Ganymede and Callisto show up as dark spots against the brighter background. Sometimes these two satellites are difficult to tell from their shadows.

Mutual phenomena between the satellites may also occur. It is possible for Io and Europa to be eclipsed by the shadow of Ganymede, for instance, and mutual occulations take place now and then.

[1] Different authorities give different figures. G. P. Kuiper, for instance, gives diameters of 2,020 miles for Io, 1,790 for Europa, 3,120 for Ganymede, and only 2,770 for Callisto. These minor discrepancies are not important; it is sufficient to say that in size the two inner satellites are comparable with the Moon, and the two outer ones with Mercury.

The first reliable observation of a mutual eclipse seems to have been made by Peek on 1926 May 22, when he watched the eclipse of Io by the shadow of Europa. Of course, fairly powerful telescopes are needed for this sort of work.

However, the eclipses of the Galilean satellites by the shadow of Jupiter itself are striking even with a small instrument. Earlier studies of them led, in fact, to the first proper determination of the velocity of light. In 1675 the Danish astronomer Ole Rømer noted that when Jupiter was relatively close to us, near opposition, the satellite eclipses were earlier than predicted, whereas when Jupiter was more remote the satellite eclipses were late. Rømer realized that this must be because the light has further to travel when Jupiter is distant. After elaborate calculations, he worked out a value for the velocity of light which was remarkably close to the true value of 186,000 miles per second.

The remaining eight satellites of Jupiter are very small and difficult to observe. Number 5, discovered by E. E. Barnard in 1892 and named Amalthea, is of definite interest. It is closer to Jupiter than any of the Galileans; it is about 112,000 miles from the planet's centre, and has a revolution period of only 12 hours. It must be subject to tremendous gravitational strain, and may well have been pulled out into an egg-like shape, though there is no definite proof, and of course its orbital speed is very great. The diameter is believed to be in the region of 150 miles, assuming that the shape does not depart too much from the spherical.

The outer satellites are generally known simply by numbers, but this is a bad system – No. 10, for instance, is much closer to Jupiter than No. 9. In view of the desperate efforts to name every tiny asteroid, this failure to give official names to the members of Jupiter's family seems rather remiss. Some years ago B. Marsden, in Britain, suggested that No. 6 should be known as Hestia; 7 as Hera; 8 as Poseidon; 9 as Hades; 10 as Demeter; 11 as Pan, and 12 as Adrastea. These names have not yet come into general use, but on the whole it would be a good thing if they did.

All these outer satellites are small; Hestia has a diameter of perhaps 100 miles, the others less than 50. Hestia, Hera, and Demeter lie at roughly 7,000,000 miles from Jupiter, and have periods of about 250 days; Adrastea, Pan, Poseidon, and Hades are between 13 and 15 million miles out, and take between 625 and 760 days to go once round Jupiter. Moreover, these four go round the wrong way – east to west instead of west to east.

When we consider small, remote satellites of this kind, we must always bear in mind the marked perturbations produced by the Sun. In fact, the paths of the satellites round Jupiter are not even approximately circular, and the orbits change with every revolution, so that the movements are hard to predict with any accuracy – in fact Poseidon was 'lost' between 1941 and 1955. As we have seen, it is quite possible that the junior moons are nothing more than captured Trojan asteroids.

Jupiter is not only the largest member of the Sun's family, but also the planet which provides the greatest scope for the serious amateur observer. With its belts, its spots, its unpredictable disturbances and its retinue of satellites, it is indeed one of the most fascinating worlds known to us.

XV Jupiter, showing three of the minor satellites. The satellites are ringed on the photograph; the planet itself is necessarily over exposed. Photo by P. J. Melotte, 1908. (*Courtesy of the Science Museum*)

XVI Saturn, in blue light (photograph, Mount Wilson and Palomar Observatories). Taken with the 200-inch Hale Reflector

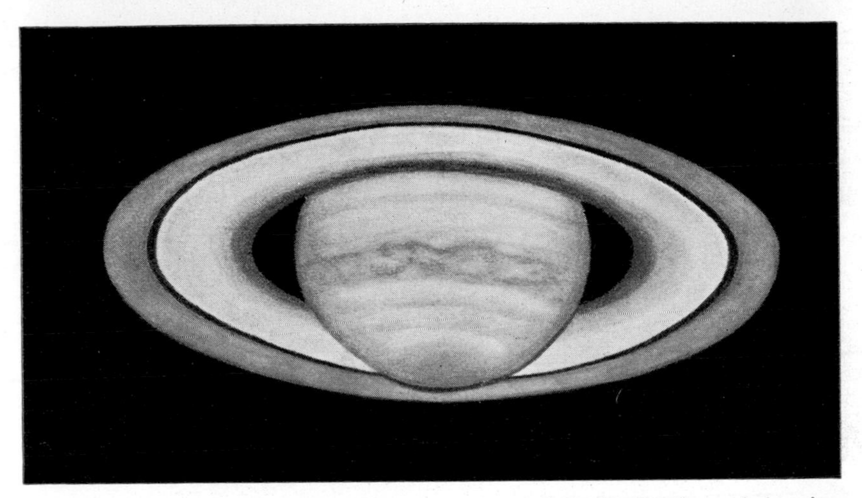

XVII Saturn. Maximum and minimum aspects of the inclination of the ring system. (Drawings by L. F. Ball)

Top. 1951 April 19. 22 hours. 10 inch × 300.
Bottom. 1958 June 9. 24 hours. 10 inch × 350.

XVIII Pluto. Two photographs showing the motion of the planet in twenty-four hours (photographs, Mount Wilson and Palomar Observatories). Taken with the 200-inch Hale Reflector

Chapter 12

Saturn

THE OUTERMOST OF THE planets known to the ancients was named by them Saturn, after Jupiter's father. It is not nearly so brilliant as Jupiter, and its yellowish hue makes it appear somewhat leaden; moreover it moves relatively slowly against the starry background. Yet when seen through a moderate telescope, it is probably the most beautiful object in the whole sky.

Everyone knows that Saturn is the planet with the rings, and it is these rings which make it unique. Jupiter is larger and more important in the Solar System as a whole, and both Venus and Mars are far more imposing when seen with the naked eye, but in its own way Saturn is unrivalled.

The splendour of the ring system tends to divert attention from the globe itself, and it is true that surface details are none too easy to make out. Basically, Saturn is not unlike Jupiter, and it too has its cloud belts and its spots, but there seems to be less general activity. Saturn is a more quiescent world than its giant brother.

Saturn is appreciably smaller than Jupiter – the equatorial diameter is 75,100 miles, the polar diameter 67,200 – and is more remote. The average distance from the Sun is 886,000,000 miles, and since its orbital velocity is only 6 miles per second Saturn takes 29 years to complete one revolution. As the axial rotation period is rapid, about 10¼ hours, a Saturnian 'year' would contain some 25,000 'days'. Neither would it be possible to divide the year into definite 'lunar months', as on Earth. Our world has only one moon, but Saturn has at least nine.

In size, Saturn is inferior only to Jupiter. Over 700 Earths could be packed inside its huge globe, but, strangely enough, it is clearly insubstantial, and its mean density is less than that of water. Its mass is 95 times as great as that of the Earth, and though its escape velocity is high (22 miles per second) its surface gravity is not. Surface gravity depends not only on the mass of a body, but also

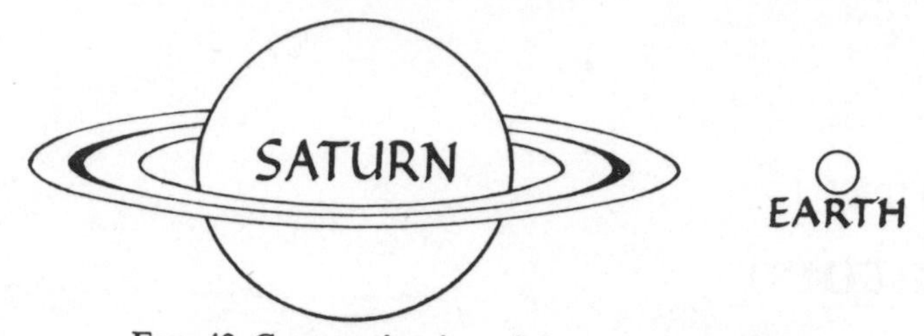

FIG. 40. Comparative sizes of Saturn and the Earth

upon its diameter; for two globes of equal mass, the smaller – and therefore denser – will have the stronger surface pull. Because Saturn is so large, its surface gravity is only a little greater than the Earth's, and a man who weighs 14 stone on Earth would weigh only about 16 stone if he could go to Saturn. Apart from Jupiter, there is no planet in the Solar System on which an Earthman would feel uncomfortably heavy.

Of course this is a theoretical case only; Saturn, like Jupiter, has a gaseous surface, and the very marked flattening shows that much of the total mass is concentrated near the centre of the globe. The outer layers must be rather rarefied. This was confirmed by an interesting observation made in 1920, when Saturn passed in front of a star, and for an appreciable time the star could still be seen through the uppermost layers.

On Wildt's model, the rocky metallic core is 28,000 miles in diameter, with the ice shell 8,000 miles deep. This leaves a depth of 16,000 miles for the atmosphere. Ramsey considers that Saturn is made up of about 60 per cent. by mass of hydrogen, and on his model there is a core of metallic hydrogen 25,300 miles across, with an 8,000-mile thick layer of more normal solid hydrogen. If so, the density of the metallic hydrogen near Saturn's centre is about twice that of water.

As Saturn is so much more remote than Jupiter, we would expect it to be colder, and the measured temperature is indeed very low – about minus 240 degrees F. Consequently, more of the ammonia has frozen out of the atmosphere, and spectroscopes record much more methane than on Jupiter. The difference is probably due to nothing more fundamental than Saturn's lower temperature, and here, as with Jupiter, most of the gas is made up of hydrogen, together with some helium and smaller quantities of other constituents.

Telescopes of fair size are needed to show much on the disk, but in general there seems to be a marked resemblance to Jupiter in one of its less active moods. Saturn's belts appear curved; the equatorial zone is usually brightish cream in colour, and once again we have the phenomenon of different parts of the planet rotating at different speeds. The equatorial period is about 10 hours 14 minutes, but in higher latitudes this may be increased by twenty minutes or more. Exact information is rather difficult to obtain.

Periodical outbursts of activity take place, particularly near the equator, comparable with a very mild Jovian outbreak, and there are times when a modest instrument is capable of showing considerable detail. However, there are no semi-permanent features comparable with the Great Red Spot on Jupiter.

Indeed, major spots are very rare indeed, and the only really striking outburst of recent years took place in 1933. In August of that year W. T. Hay, a British amateur (Will Hay, the stage and screen comedian), discovered a prominent white spot in the equatorial zone. It rapidly became very conspicuous, and as a boy of nine I well remember seeing it with my 3-inch refractor. It gradually lengthened, and the portion of the disk following it darkened; subsequently the forward edge of the spot became diffuse in outline, the following end staying sharp and clear-cut. To quote H. Spencer Jones, the appearance suggested 'a mass of matter thrown up from an eruption below the visible surface, encountering a current travelling with greater speed than the erupted matter, which was carried forward with the current while still being fed from the following end'. However, the spot did not last for long. It faded quickly, and in a few months had disappeared completely. White spots have been seen since, but all have been much inferior to Hay's in size and brilliance.

The precise cause of these outbreaks is not known, but the spots seem certainly to be of the same nature as those on Jupiter. Saturn's relative quiescence is due to its lower temperature and lesser density. Colours on the disk have been reported from time to time, and some observers have described greens, browns and even reds, but personally I have never seen anything of the sort.

It is the ring-system which makes Saturn unique in its glory, and even though the rings are not of real importance they have many points of interest. A small telescope will show them, though the more delicate features require a large aperture. They have been known ever since the seventeenth century, and Galileo observed them, though not clearly enough to make out just what they were.

In 1659 Christiaan Huygens, a Dutch astronomer, issued a famous anagram[1] in which he announced that Saturn was surrounded by 'a flat ring, which nowhere touches the body of the planet, and is inclined to the ecliptic'. He was correct as far as he went, but it is now known that there are three principal rings. A schematic drawing of the ring system is given here.

The system is of vast extent. The outermost ring, known as Ring A, is 10,000 miles wide; then comes a well-marked gap, known as Cassini's Division, with a width of 1,700 miles, and then Ring B,

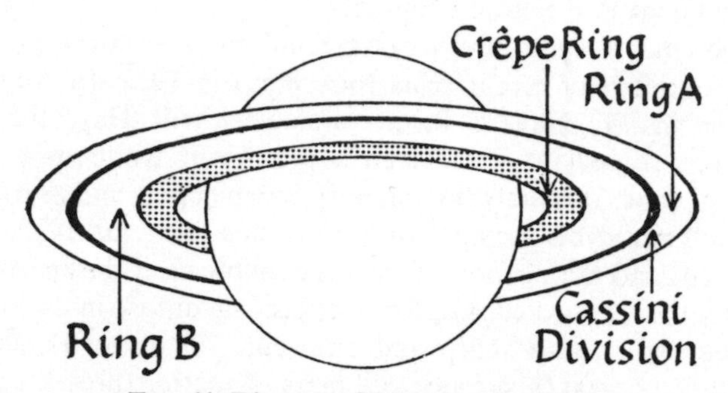

FIG. 41. Diagram of Saturn's ring system

16,000 miles wide. The 'ring' described by Huygens was a combination of A and B. His telescope was not powerful enough to reveal the gap between them, and this feature was first described in 1675 by G. D. Cassini, an Italian astronomer who had been called to Paris to direct the new observatory there.

Rings A and B are not alike. B is much the brighter of the two, and is less transparent; even a small telescope of good performance will show the difference, and the Cassini Division itself may be seen with a 3-inch refractor when the rings are suitably tilted.

Inside Ring B, between it and the planet, is a third ring, named

[1] The anagram consisted of a number of letters in alphabetical order, which, when rearranged, formed the Latin sentence: *Annulo cingitur, tenui, plano, nusquam cohærente, ad eclipticam inclinato.* In those days, before the laws of copyright were drawn up, it was the custom to announce discoveries in anagram form. Galileo had never succeeded in finding out the true nature of the rings, and had been under the impression that Saturn must be a triple planet.

Ring C, more generally known as the Crêpe or Dusky Ring. It was first recognized in 1850 by two independent observers, W. Bond in America and W. R. Dawes in England, and is comparatively inconspicuous; it is much less luminous than A or B, and is transparent enough for the globe of Saturn to be seen through it.

It is rather strange that the Crêpe Ring should have remained undetected for so long. Herschel, the greatest observer of his time, paid a great deal of attention to Saturn and observed most of the features which we know today; but although one or two of his drawings do show the Crêpe Ring, he failed to recognize it for what it is. Nowadays it is not a really delicate object, and the suggestion has been made that it has brightened up since Herschel's time. On the whole, however, this seems unlikely, since such an increase in brilliancy would be very hard to account for.

The Crêpe Ring is 10,000 miles wide, and between it and the planet is a 'clear' area 9,000 miles in width, into which the Earth would fit quite comfortably. It is worth adding that from time to time there have been reports of an outer dusky ring, beyond Ring A, but it has not been confirmed, and its real existence is doubtful. I have made several searches for it, using the 33-inch refractor at Meudon, but without any success.

The shadows cast by the rings upon the disk of Saturn are easily seen, and unwary observers have often mistaken the main shadow for a surface belt. The disk, too, can cast shadow on the rings.

The ring system is of course circular, and has a total diameter of around 170,000 miles. Yet the rings are remarkably thin; their thickness is probably not more than 10 miles, certainly not more than 40. If we reduce Saturn in scale to a globe with an equatorial diameter of 5 inches, the ring-span will be one foot, but the ring thickness will be only $\frac{1}{1500}$ of an inch.

This thinness has important consequences so far as we are concerned. When the rings are edge-on to us, as was the case in 1950 and will be again in 1966, they almost disappear. The Earth is passing through the plane of the ring-system, and in a small or moderate telescope Saturn appears simply as a disk crossed by belts. A really large instrument will generally show the ring-system as a hair-thin line of light, but not always. In November 1920, for instance, E. E. Barnard, using the largest refractor in the world (the Yerkes 40-inch), lost the rings completely for over a week.

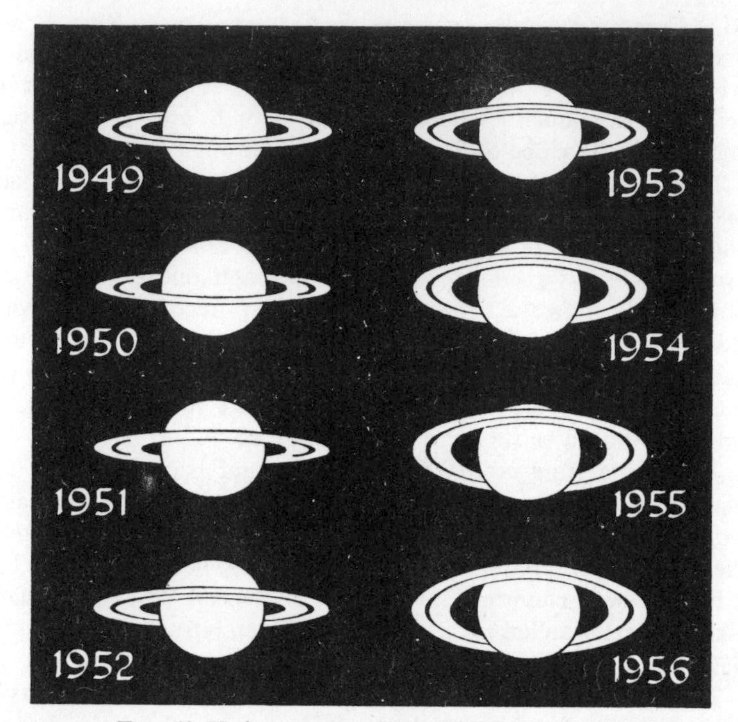

FIG. 42. Various aspects of Saturn's rings, 1949–1956

Saturn's rings lie exactly in the plane of the planet's equator, which is tilted to the Earth's orbit at an angle of 28 degrees. Sometimes we see the north side of the rings, sometimes the south; when best displayed, as was the case in 1958 and 1959, the rings may hide the polar region of the disk. A simple model will serve to show just what happens. Take a tennis-ball, and make a paper ring to go round it, as shown in the diagram. When the ball is held so that the paper ring is edge-on, nothing will be seen except a thin line crossing the ball and projecting to either side. By tilting the ball suitably, all aspects of the rings can be reproduced. It must however be borne in mind that the paper ring is thicker, on this scale, than Saturn's ring-system really is.

The two brightest rings, A and B, look so solid when viewed through a telescope that it was natural for the early observers to regard them as continuous. Unfortunately for this theory, the English

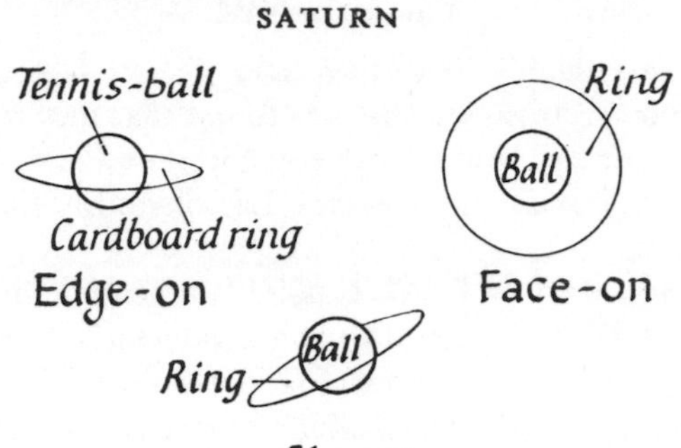

FIG. 43. Tennis-ball model to show the changing aspects of Saturn's rings

mathematician Clerk Maxwell showed in 1859 that no such ring could manage to survive, since the whole system lies within the danger-zone of Saturn known technically as Roche's Limit.

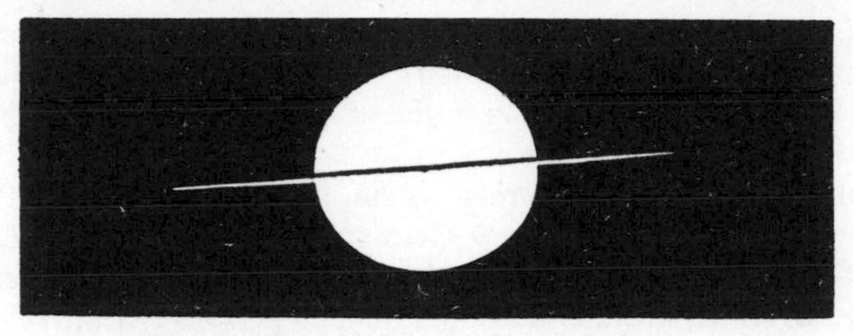

FIG. 44. Saturn edge-on
1951 June 10. 22 h. Patrick Moore: 8½ in. Refl. ×300.

It is worth elaborating a little on this danger-zone, since it is important to theoretical astronomers. In 1848 Édouard Roche, of France, had calculated that if a solid body of normal density comes within a certain distance of a planet, it cannot escape being broken up by the planet's gravitational pull. The limiting distance depends on the size and mass of the planet concerned. In the case of Saturn, the rings are within Roche's Limit, and therefore cannot be solid or liquid. Any such ring would be literally torn to pieces.

J. J. Cassini, second Director of the Paris Observatory, made the shrewd suggestion that the rings might be composed of numerous small solid particles – tiny moonlets, in fact – each revolving round the planet in its own individual orbit. This has turned out to be the correct explanation. It fits all the facts, and explains why the inner parts of the system move round Saturn more rapidly than the outer.

The rings are highly reflective, and G. P. Kuiper, who has examined them spectroscopically, has found that they must be either made up of ice or else coated with some icy substance. We can only guess as to the sizes of the particles, but obviously they cannot be very large.

The gap discovered by G. D. Cassini is a genuine break between Rings A and B. Clearly, then, this is a zone which the ring-particles tend to avoid, and it is now known that Saturn's satellites are responsible. The chief agent is Mimas, which moves round the planet only 30,000 miles or so beyond the outer edge of Ring A – not so very far outside Roche's Limit. Mimas takes 22·6 hours to go once round Saturn. Any particle moving in Cassini's Division would have a period of exactly half this, or 11·3 hours. Therefore, the pull of Mimas will have a regular and cumulative effect upon such a particle, and will drive it out of the Division into a different orbit; in other words, Mimas keeps the Cassini Division zone swept clear. Some of the other satellites play their part, and it seems that the diffuse appearance of the Crêpe Ring is due to the action of the fourth and fifth moons, Dione and Rhea.

Other divisions in the ring-system have been reported. One, announced by the last-century German astronomer Johann Encke and therefore named Encke's Division, lies in Ring A, and is said to be visible with moderate telescopes, though personally I always find it a difficult object. It may not be a true gap in the sense that Cassini's is, and other minor divisions reported by various observers are probably more in the nature of surface ripples.

It is interesting to speculate as to how the rings were formed. They may be due to a 'celestial shipwreck', the destroyed 'vessel' being a former satellite which came within the Roche Limit for Saturn and paid the supreme penalty of being broken up and spread round the planet in a swarm of fragments. An alternative idea is that the rings never formed a larger body, and that they, as well as Saturn's five inner satellites, condensed out of a former surround of matter. At present we cannot be certain one way or the other; but however the ring-system came into being, it is unrivalled in the Solar System.

Of Saturn's nine satellites, the most important is Titan, which is of planetary dimensions. Its diameter appears to be about 3,500 miles, so that it is the largest satellite known, and is intermediate in

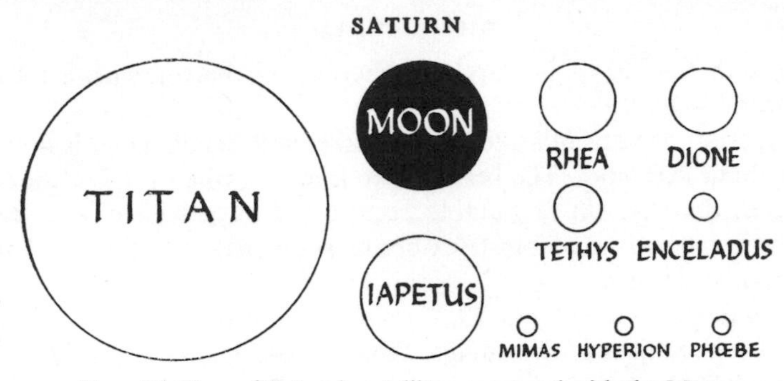

FIG. 45. Sizes of Saturn's satellites compared with the Moon

size between Mercury and Mars.[1] It is much more massive than our Moon, and has an escape velocity of over 2 miles per second. Moreover it has an atmosphere, discovered spectroscopically by Kuiper in 1944. Yet Titan is a forbidding world; it is intensely cold, and the atmosphere consists largely of methane, so that it cannot support even the most primitive forms of life as we know it. The period is almost 16 days, and the distance from Saturn exceeds 750,000 miles.

Though Titan is large, it is also so remote that surface details are excessively hard to make out; only giant telescopes will show them. In 1953 H. P. Wilkins, using the Meudon 33-inch refractor, recorded two dusky patches, but with the same instrument I was unable to see them with any certainty. The colour of the disk is distinctly yellowish.

Titan was discovered by Christiaan Huygens as long ago as 1655, and can be seen with a small telescope, but the remaining satellites are considerably smaller and fainter. The five inner members of the family, Mimas, Enceladus, Tethys, Dione, and Rhea, have diameters ranging from perhaps 1,100 miles (Rhea) down to 300 miles (Mimas), but all these values are extremely uncertain, and may be considerably in error. According to estimates by Kuiper, Mimas and Enceladus are less dense than water, so that, like Callisto, they may be largely icy in nature. Tethys is of rather the same type, but Dione is almost three times as dense as water, and is much more massive.

Rhea may be seen with a 3-inch refractor, and I have also picked up Dione and Tethys with a telescope of this aperture, but not easily. Mimas and Enceladus are both smaller and closer in, so that they are decidedly elusive; both were discovered by William Herschel in

[1] Different authorities give different estimates; Kuiper prefers 2,990 miles.

1789 with the aid of his largest telescope, a reflector with a focal length of 40 feet.

Hyperion, the seventh satellite, is smaller still. Its diameter is probably about 200 miles. The best time to find it is when it lies close to Titan in the sky. On favourable occasions I have seen it with my 12½-inch reflector, and most textbooks state that it is fainter than is actually the case.[1]

Iapetus, discovered by G. D. Cassini in 1671, is perhaps the most interesting member of the satellite family. Here again the diameter is extremely uncertain, but may be between 1,500 and 2,000 miles, in which event it is not a great deal smaller than our Moon. It is a long way from Saturn - over 2,000,000 miles - and has a revolution period of 79 days.

The main peculiarity of Iapetus is that it varies in brightness. When at its greatest distance west of Saturn in the sky it is superior to Rhea, and is visible in a 3-inch refractor. About five weeks later, when it is east of the planet, the brightness has fallen away so markedly that Iapetus is much fainter than either Tethys or Dione. These variations are very pronounced, and have been known for many years.

Obviously, some surface peculiarity is at the root of this queer behaviour. One important fact is that Iapetus, like all other major satellites, has a captured rotation, so that its 'day' is 79 times as long as ours, and the same face is presented to Saturn all the time - which does at least explain why the variations in brightness are regular. F. L. Whipple has suggested that one side reflects more efficiently than the other, and that in the remote past Iapetus was either disfigured by collision with a wandering body or else discoloured by gaseous outbursts from Saturn. Yet on the latter theory it is hard to see why Iapetus, and Iapetus only, should have been so affected.

An alternative idea is that some sort of surface deposit is responsible. If Iapetus retains any atmosphere, the gaseous mantle would presumably freeze during the long night, so that the brightness at western elongation could be due to the solar rays striking this frozen deposit. Unfortunately we still have to explain why only Iapetus behaves in such a way, and in any case it seems most unlikely that the

[1] According to my estimates, made between 1946 and 1961, this also applies to Tethys, Dione, and Iapetus.

escape velocity is high enough for any atmosphere to be retained. On the whole, it is simpler to suppose that for some unknown reason one hemisphere is darker than the other.

The outermost of Saturn's satellites, discovered photographically by W. H. Pickering in 1898, is named Phœbe. Although very small, with an estimated diameter of only 150 miles, it has an interesting orbit, fairly circular but highly inclined; and it is so far from Saturn – over 8,000,000 miles – that it takes a year and a half to complete one revolution. Like the outermost members of the Jovian family, it moves in a retrograde or 'wrong-way' direction, and may possibly be a captured asteroid rather than a genuine satellite.

Pickering's discovery was made with a 24-inch telescope at Arequipa in Peru, the southern station of Harvard College Observatory. Six years later Pickering announced that he had found a tenth satellite. He named it Themis, and computed an orbit according to which the distance was intermediate between those of Titan and Hyperion. Unfortunately no further photographs of it have been secured, and most astronomers now consider that it does not exist at all, so that it – like the planet Vulcan – must be regarded as a 'ghost'.

At our present stage of technical development it is obviously premature to consider launching probe-rockets to Saturn; the distance is much too great, and a round trip would take years. In the future, such probes may well be dispatched, but whether manned vehicles will ever visit the Saturnian system is more problematical. We can only hope so, since a close-up view of the ringed planet would be breathtaking indeed. Meanwhile, we can at least enjoy the spectacle from our home on Earth. As Saturn swims into the telescopic field – remote, lonely, and unutterably magnificent – it makes a picture which no one who has seen it will ever be likely to forget.

Chapter 13

Uranus

WE DO NOT KNOW who first noticed Mars, Jupiter, and the other brilliant planets. At least it is certain that the discovery must have been made before the start of recorded history, and by Greek times the movements of the planets against the starry background had been closely studied. According to the old theories, the Earth lay at rest in the centre of the universe, and there were five planets going round it – Mercury, Venus, Mars, Jupiter, and Saturn. These five, together with the Sun and Moon, made up seven 'planetary' bodies. Seven was the magical number, and therefore it seemed only proper that there should be seven planets. What, in fact, could be more reasonable?

Kepler had his doubts, and thought that there might be a small planet moving round the Sun between the orbits of Mars and Jupiter. Titius and Bode came to the same conclusion. Yet it does not seem to have occurred to anyone that there might be a planet far out in the twilight regions beyond Saturn, and the discovery made by a young musician-astronomer in the year 1781 took the whole scientific world by surprise.

William Herschel, the man responsible, was a Hanoverian who had settled in England and had become an organist. About 1772 he began to carry out active work in astronomy, and between that date and the end of his life, in 1822, he accomplished a great deal. He became by far the most skilful instrument-maker of his time; he was the founder of true 'stellar astronomy', the study of the stars themselves, and he was the first to give a reasonably accurate picture of the shape of our star-system or Galaxy.

On 1781 March 13, Herschel was busy examining some faint stars in the constellation Gemini, the group which contains the famous 'twins' Castor and Pollux. In his own words, he 'perceived one star which appeared visibly larger than all the rest', and 'suspected it to be a comet'. At that moment he had no idea of the great importance of the discovery. When the object's path was worked out, however, it became clear that what Herschel had found was not a comet at all, but a new major planet.

It has often been said that the discovery was sheer chance, but this view is unfair to Herschel. He was engaged upon a systematic review of the entire sky, and as he pointed out in a letter written to a friend of his, Dr Hutton: 'Had business prevented me that evening, I must have found it the next, and the goodness of my telescope was such that I must have perceived its visible planetary disk as soon as I looked at it.' As a matter of fact, his telescope was only a modest $6\frac{1}{5}$ reflector of his own manufacture, and his confidence in his ability to detect anything unusual is fitting testimony not only to his patience but also to his eyesight.

Herschel was not the first to record the new planet. It had been seen on several previous occasions, and the first Astronomer Royal, John Flamsteed, had noted it six times between 1690 and 1715 without realizing that it was anything but an ordinary star. Keen-sighted persons can just see it with the naked eye, provided that they know exactly where to look.

It is interesting to recall that the discovery could hardly have been delayed for more than twenty extra years. Had Herschel failed to find the planet, it could not have escaped the search organized by Schröter and von Zach in the first years of the nineteenth century. It would indeed have been remarkable if the 'asteroid hunters' had been rewarded by the detection of a new major planet far beyond the known limits of the Solar System.

Several rather unsuitable names were suggested for the new body, but before long Bode's proposal of 'Uranus' came into general use. For Herschel, the discovery was the turning-point of his career. He received a royal grant which enabled him to give up music as a profession, and henceforward he devoted all his time to science – to the great benefit of astronomy in general, stellar astronomy in particular. Every possible honour came his way. He was awarded a knighthood, became the King's Astronomer, and at the very end of his life was elected first president of the newly founded Royal Astronomical Society.

Uranus is very remote. Its mean distance from the Sun is 1,782,000,000 miles, and it moves at only about 4 miles per second, so that it takes 84 years to complete one revolution. This means that its discovery by Herschel took place only just over two 'Uranian years' ago.

In size it is intermediate between Saturn and the Earth, but it certainly ranks as a giant. The diameter is 29,300 miles, and its polar

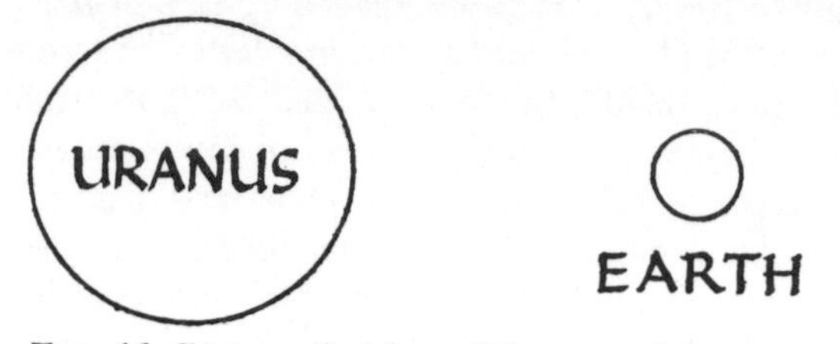

FIG. 46. Comparative sizes of Uranus and the Earth

flattening is about as marked as Jupiter's. It is denser than water, and much denser than Saturn. Yet though its globe could contain 50 bodies the size of the Earth, Uranus has only 14·6 times the mass of our world. The escape velocity is 13·9 miles per second, and yet the surface gravity is only fractionally greater than that of the Earth. A man who weighs 13 stone here would weigh only 14 stone if he could go to Uranus.

Wildt has worked out a model for Uranus much as he has done for Jupiter and Saturn, and has found that the rock core has a diameter of 14,000 miles, with a 6,000-mile ice layer and a gaseous mantle 3,000 miles deep. Ramsey considers that Uranus is 'presumably composed of water, methane and ammonia, together with terrestrial materials'.

Analysis of the outer cloud-layers is much more difficult than for Saturn, since Uranus is not only much smaller but also twice as far off. Here again it is probable that the 'atmosphere' is mainly hydrogen, together with some helium. Spectroscopically, hydrogen compounds are much in evidence; there is a considerable amount of methane, but only a trace of ammonia, since at this low temperature (around −310 degrees F.) most of the ammonia must be in a frozen state.

Uranus, like Jupiter and Saturn, spins rapidly upon its axis. The best value so far obtained is 10·8 hours, in which case there are about 65,000 'days' in each Uranian year. Probably the rotation is quickest in the equatorial zone, but we have no precise information.

The most peculiar fact about Uranus is the tilt of its axis. As we have seen, most of the large planets rotate with their axes not greatly

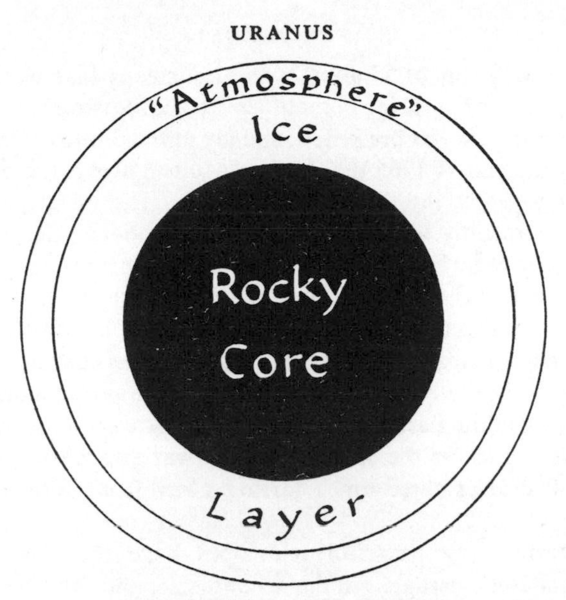

FIG. 47. Wildt's model of Uranus

inclined to the perpendiculars to their orbits. The Earth, Mars, Saturn and Neptune have inclinations of between 23° and 30°, and this may also be true of Venus, while that of Jupiter is less (just over 3°). Uranus has its own way of behaving. The axial tilt is actually more than a right angle, and so the rotation is technically retrograde.

As a result of this, the 'seasons' on Uranus are peculiar, to put it

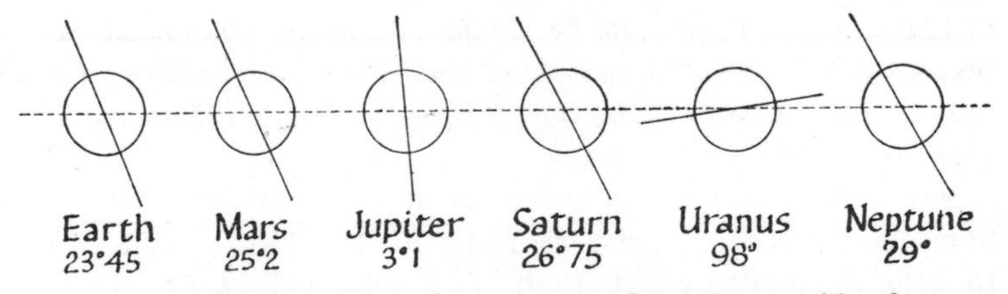

FIG. 48. Inclinations of the axes of rotation of the planets, with reference to their orbits

mildly. First much of the northern hemisphere, then much of the southern, will be plunged into Stygian blackness for 21 Earth-years at a time, with a corresponding 'midnight sun' in the opposite hemisphere. For the rest of the revolution period, 48 terrestrial years, conditions will be less unfamiliar.

The unusual tilt of Uranus' axis also means that we sometimes look straight at a pole, sometimes at the equator. In 1946, for instance, the pole was presented, and lay at the centre of the apparent disk. By the end of 1965 the equator will run across the disk-centre, with the poles at the limbs to either side. The surface appearance must consequently be most odd, but unfortunately the planet is so remote that even large telescopes will not show much.

Small instruments will reveal a small greenish disk, quite unstarlike. I well remember an interesting event in May 1955, when Uranus passed close to Jupiter in the sky; it was considerably larger than any of the Galilean satellites, but its disk was also much dimmer. At that period the Earth, Jupiter, and Uranus were more or less lined up, with Jupiter in the middle, and it was strange to reflect that Uranus was over three times farther away from Jupiter than we are!

Observers using powerful telescopes have recorded a whitish equatorial zone, perhaps similar to Saturn's, and faint belts; but all these features are difficult to make out.

Uranus fluctuates somewhat in brilliancy. Some variations are of course to be expected, since there are several factors to be taken into account. When Uranus is near perihelion, it will be more brightly lit than when at its farthest from the Sun, and will moreover be closer to the Earth. There is also a complication due to the sharp inclination of the axis, since when the pole faces us – as in 1946 – the apparent surface area will not be the same as when we are looking straight at the equator. (This can be demonstrated by holding up an egg first with the thin end presented and then broadside-on, though naturally the relative flattening of Uranus is much less than in the case of the egg.)

Yet these fairly obvious factors do not account for all the variations actually recorded, and the rest must be due to physical causes. In 1917 W. W. Campbell, at the Lick Observatory, found a small regular change due to the axial rotation; astronomers at Potsdam reported another, due to changes in the reflecting power of Uranus' atmosphere over a period of years. Considerable disturbances may well be taking place in the surface layers, and Uranus may be fully as active as Saturn. More detailed information is needed, and it is a pity that Uranus is so far away that giant apertures are required to show it even moderately well.

As befits its status as a senior member of the Sun's family, Uranus is accompanied by a retinue of satellites. Herschel believed that he had discovered six, but for once he was mistaken; four of his 'satellites' were in reality faint stars, and only two, those now known as Titania and Oberon, were genuine attendants. Two more, Ariel and Umbriel, were found in 1851 by the English amateur William Lassell, while the fifth and faintest, Miranda, was detected by G. P. Kuiper at the McDonald Observatory, in Texas, as recently as 1948.

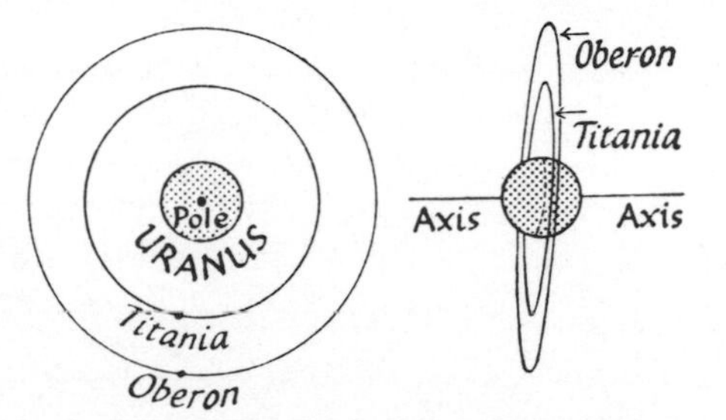

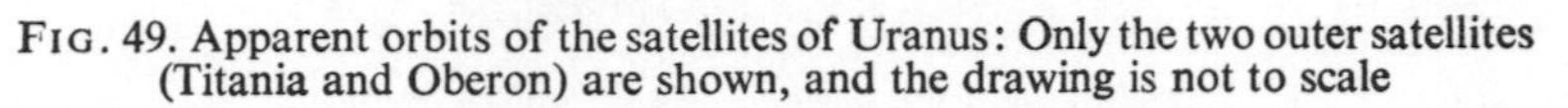
FIG. 49. Apparent orbits of the satellites of Uranus: Only the two outer satellites (Titania and Oberon) are shown, and the drawing is not to scale

All five satellites revolve almost in the plane of Uranus' equator; consequently their orbits appear circular when the planet's pole is presented to us, almost straight up-and-down lines when the equator is displayed. Their distances from Uranus range from 76,000 miles (Miranda) to 364,000 miles (Oberon).

The brilliancies of the four main satellites have often been underestimated. It is true that they are not easy objects, but in 1947 W. H. Steavenson examined them with his 30-inch reflector at Cambridge and found that they are brighter than had been generally supposed. He also found that both Titania and Oberon vary considerably, and there may be some similarity between their behaviour and that of Iapetus, though it is still uncertain whether the variations are regular or not.

Adopting Steavenson's revised estimates of brilliancy, and assuming that the satellites are of normal reflecting power, it seems that Ariel, Titania, and Oberon may be between 1,300 and 1,800 miles in diameter, Umbriel between 700 and 900, and Miranda 200; but these values are most unreliable. At any rate, the escape velocities must be low, so that none of the five can have retained any appreciable mantle of atmosphere.

We need not waste time in working out the details of a rocket to Uranus. The 'seventh planet' is so remote that we cannot be surprised at our lack of knowledge about its surface features, and as a world it must be lonely beyond all understanding.

Chapter 14

Neptune

FAR AWAY IN THE depths of space, a thousand million miles beyond Uranus, lies the last of the giant planets – Neptune, a world so remote that we cannot see it at all without using a telescope. Neptunian astronomers, if they existed, could know nothing about the Earth; but strangely enough, terrestrial astronomers knew that Neptune existed even before they actually observed it. The story of its discovery is certainly worth re-telling.

The key to the problem was provided by Uranus. As we have seen, Uranus had been recorded several times before Herschel saw it in 1781; Flamsteed noted it half a dozen times, and so did a French astronomer named Le Monnier. Flamsteed never checked his observations, and Le Monnier was not blessed with an orderly and methodical mind. However, when mathematicians came to work out the orbit of the newly found Uranus, the old observations came in most useful – even one of Le Monnier's which was pencilled on the back of a bag which had once contained hair perfume![1]

Altogether, records of Uranus extended back over a hundred years before 1781, more than one complete revolution of the planet, and it should have been possible to calculate a reliable orbit. Unfortunately the old observations did not seem to fit properly with those made after 1781. Something was wrong somewhere, and eventually a French mathematician, Alexis Bouvard, rejected the old observations altogether and worked out a new orbit based only upon positions measured after Uranus had been recognized as a planet.

Even this would not do. Uranus refused to behave; it persistently

[1] Le Monnier seemed fated to miss perpetuating his name. While engaged upon cataloguing the stars near the north celestial pole, he introduced an entirely new constellation, Tarandus (the Reindeer), which was promptly forgotten. Le Monnier was undoubtedly a clever scientist, and did much valuable work, but it is said of him that he quarrelled with every person with whom he came in contact.

strayed from its predicted path. Up to 1822 it seemed to move too rapidly, while after 1822 it lagged. It became painfully clear that there must be some unknown factor to be taken into account.

As we have seen, each planet perturbs its fellows; thus the Earth is appreciably perturbed by Venus and Mars, and to a lesser extent by the more remote planets also. The most powerful known disturbing agents so far as Uranus was concerned were Saturn and Jupiter, but Bouvard had allowed for them both, and still Uranus wandered.

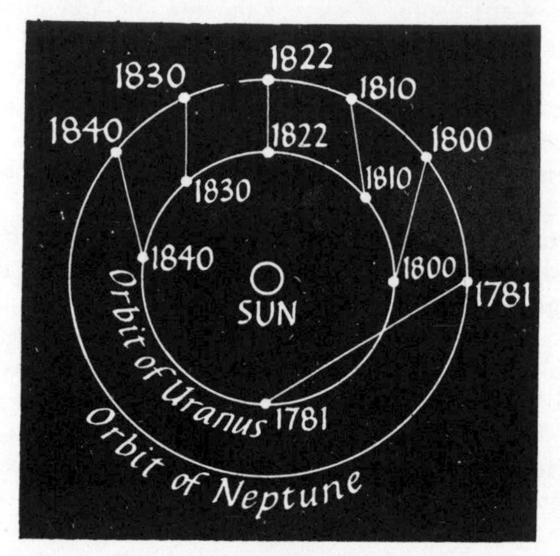

FIG. 50. Neptune's pull on Uranus

In 1834 the Rev. T. J. Hussey, the Rector of Hayes in Kent, made a most interesting suggestion. Suppose that an unknown planet were pulling on Uranus? This might account for the irregularities of motion, and by 'working backwards', so to speak, it might be possible to track down the planet responsible.

Hussey went so far as to write a letter to George (afterwards Sir George) Airy, the Astronomer Royal of the time, but Airy was not encouraging. However, in 1841 a young Cambridge student, John Couch Adams, made up his mind to attack the whole problem as soon as he had taken his mathematical degree. He passed the final examinations – brilliantly – in 1843, and then began to study the movements of Uranus in earnest. By the end of the year he had worked out just where the unknown planet ought to be, and, naturally enough, he sent his results to Airy.

Now began a series of misfortunes which led to a most undignified dispute in after years. Airy, partly through a lack of confidence in Adams and partly through a misunderstanding, took no action. Delay followed delay, until in 1846 Urbain Le Verrier, a French astronomer, published a memoir which showed that he had approached the problem much as Adams had done, with similar results.

As soon as Airy saw Le Verrier's memoir, he asked two observers – Professor Challis, at Cambridge, and an amateur named William Lassell – to begin searching in the place indicated by Adams. Still there were delays. Challis had no suitable star-maps of the area, while Lassell was rendered *hors de combat* by a sprained ankle. Challis actually recorded the object he was seeking on August 4 and again on August 12, but he failed to check the observations, and before he had done so Johann Galle and Heinrich d'Arrest, working at Berlin Observatory upon Le Verrier's calculations, had found and identified the new planet.

Adams had been the first to forecast the planet's position; Le Verrier's work had led to the first actual identification, and both mathematicians were deserving of the highest praise. Unhappily, they were made the centre of a childish squabble about priority which is best forgotten – and in which neither of the principals took much part. Wrangles of this nature cannot be defended. It is the discovery which matters, not the man who makes it.

Neptune, as the new planet was named, proved to be a giant, very similar to Uranus but much more remote. Its average distance from the Sun is 2,793,000,000 miles, and it has a period of 164¾ years, so that not until the year 2011 will it return to the part of its orbit at which it was first recognized by Galle and d'Arrest. The inclination of its axis is normal (about 29 degrees), so that the peculiar seasonal effects of Uranus do not occur. The rotation period is rather uncertain. Most authorities give 15·8 hours, but the latest information shows that this may be too long, and that 14 hours is a more probable value.

As soon as Neptune was discovered, the orbit of Uranus was recalculated, and this time the old observations of Flamsteed and Le Monnier fitted almost perfectly into place. It is worth noting that

Neptune was in 'opposition', so far as Uranus was concerned, in 1822; the Sun, Uranus, and Neptune were then almost in line, with Uranus in the middle position. Before 1822, Neptune was tending to pull Uranus along; after 1822 the effect was reversed. Had Uranus and Neptune been on opposite sides of the Sun during the early nineteenth century, the disturbing effects upon Uranus would have been inappreciable, and Neptune's discovery would have been considerably delayed.

Until the last few years Neptune was believed to be larger than Uranus, but new measures show that it is smaller, with a diameter of 27,700 miles. It is, however, the more massive of the two. Its mass is 17·6 times that of the Earth, and it is much the densest of the four giant planets, which accounts for the fact that it is only slightly flattened at the poles. The surface gravity is also higher than that of Uranus. A man who weighs 13 stone on Earth would weigh over 18 stone on Neptune.

According to Wildt, the rocky core is 12,000 miles in diameter, the ice layer 6,000 miles thick, and the outer gas 2,000 miles deep; Ramsey considers that Neptune's composition is very much the same as that of Uranus. Certainly the outer clouds contain a good deal of methane. Ammonia has not been detected, since the very low temperature, about −360 degrees F., is enough to freeze practically all the ammonia out of the atmosphere.

Surface details on Neptune are extremely hard to make out. A brightish equatorial zone has been suspected, but we have to confess that we have virtually no information.

Neptune has only two known satellites, but both are of unusual interest. The first, Triton, was discovered by Lassell only three weeks after Neptune itself had been found, and is one of the largest and most massive satellites in the Solar System. The diameter is believed to be in the region of 3,000 miles; the escape velocity must be reasonably high, and the presence of a methane atmosphere has been suspected. A moderate telescope will show it, since it is brighter than any of the satellites of Uranus. The orbit is almost circular, but sharply inclined; the direction of movement is retrograde.

The second satellite, Nereid, was discovered by G. P. Kuiper in 1949. It is very minute – probably about 200 miles in diameter – and has an extraordinary orbit, so eccentric that the distance from Neptune changes from 867,000 miles to over 6,000,000 miles. The period is almost a year, and the movement is direct. It is so faint that it has never been seen visually, though it has left its image upon photographic plates.

If Uranus is lonely and remote, Neptune is even more so. A small telescope will show it in the guise of a faint, rather bluish star; larger instruments will reveal a definite disk, but we cannot expect to obtain anything like a satisfactory view of the bitterly cold 'clouds' which mask the outermost giant.

Chapter 15

Pluto

WITH THE DISCOVERY OF Neptune, the Solar System seemed to be complete once more. The wanderings of Uranus had been accounted for; the old observations of Flamsteed and Le Monnier had fallen into place, and all the irregularities which had so puzzled Bouvard had been explained. Such was the general opinion for almost half a century. And then – very slowly, very slightly – Uranus started to wander again.

The differences between the predicted and actual positions were so small that they might have been due to observational errors. Yet it was possible that the cause was more fundamental, and Percival Lowell, best remembered for his theories about Mars but also a first-class mathematician, came to the conclusion that there must be another planet waiting to be discovered. Accordingly, he commenced to work out just where it should be, much as Adams and Le Verrier had done for Neptune.

Although the unknown planet was presumably beyond Neptune's orbit, and would therefore affect Neptune more strongly than Uranus, Lowell preferred to base his calculations upon the wanderings of the inner of the two giants. This was because Neptune's movements were less well known. It had been discovered later, and had completed about one-third of a revolution round the Sun since Galle and d'Arrest had first recognized it in 1846. Two pre-discovery positions made by the French astronomer Lalande in 1795 were available, but were of rather dubious accuracy.

Lowell was well equipped. He had built his observatory at Flagstaff, in Arizona, specially for planetary work, and he started hunting in 1905, though his final calculations were not published until 1914. 'Planet X', as he called the unknown body, was thought to lie just under 4,000 million miles from the Sun, moving in a rather eccentric orbit and completing one revolution in 282 years. As the disturbances affecting Uranus were so small, Lowell thought that it must be a small planet rather than a giant, with a mass perhaps six times that of the Earth.

When Lowell died, two years after the publication of his final memoir, Planet X was still unfound, and the search was temporarily given up. Meanwhile a similar investigation, based this time upon the movements of Neptune, had been carried out by another American astronomer, W. H. Pickering. Pickering's results agreed well with those of Lowell, and in 1919 Milton Humason, at the Mount Wilson Observatory, began to search in the position indicated.

Despite the probable faintness of Planet X, Humason's task was in some ways easier than that of Challis seventy years before. Challis had to check each star visually, and the fact that he had no proper chart was one of the reasons why he was not the first to identify Neptune. Humason, however, could make use of photography.

If an area of the sky is photographed twice, with an interval of one or two days between the exposures, the stars will stay in the same positions relative to each other, but a planet will be seen to have moved. All that need be done, therefore, is to check the two photographs, and see whether any 'star' has shifted. The process is laborious to a degree, but at least it is straightforward.

To Pickering's disappointment, Humason was not successful, and Planet X obstinately refused to show itself. After a time the search was given up, but in 1929 astronomers at Lowell's observatory – Flagstaff – returned to it, armed with a 13-inch refractor and an ingenious instrument known as a 'blink-microscope' for comparing exposed photographic plates. Clyde Tombaugh, then a young assistant observer, took charge of the search, and in early 1930 he came across a suspicious object which soon proved to be the long-awaited planet.

Pluto, as it was named, was much fainter than anticipated, which is certainly why Lowell had not found it during his earlier searches. Humason's failure, however, was due to sheer bad luck. During 1919 he had actually photographed the planet twice, but one image fell upon a flaw in the plate, while the other was hopelessly masked by an inconvenient star. In all respects apart from brightness, Pluto fitted in well with Lowell's Planet X. The distance was rather less, the orbital eccentricity greater, the period of revolution shorter; but on the whole Lowell's forecasts had been pleasingly accurate.

Unfortunately, the discoveries which followed were most disconcerting. Pluto proved to be not only faint, but also surprisingly small and lacking in mass. Instead of being six times as massive as the Earth, it began to look as though the Earth were actually the more massive of the two. The implications of this were far-reaching. A comparatively minor body of this sort could have hardly any measurable effects upon giants such as Uranus and Neptune. Could the discovery have been due to pure chance, after all?

The orbit, too, had its peculiarities. When at perihelion, Pluto is actually closer in to the Sun than Neptune ever goes, though for

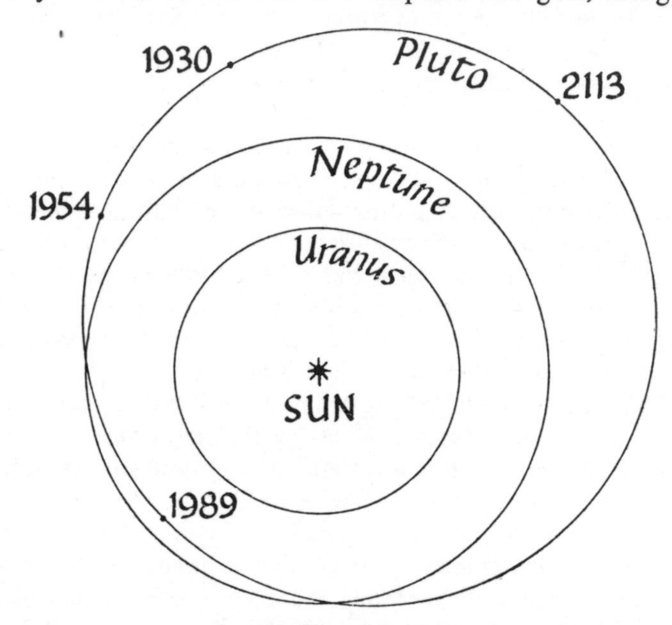

FIG. 51. The orbit of Pluto

most of its revolution period of 248 years it is much more remote. The orbit is shown in the diagram. It is worth noting that there is no danger of a collision with Neptune, since the orbit of Pluto is inclined at the comparatively sharp angle of 17 degrees.

Altogether, Pluto proved to be a baffling little world. The most important thing was to find out its mass, and, assuming a normal density, the best way of doing this was to measure its diameter. However, even the 100-inch Mount Wilson reflector was unable to show a proper disk, and nothing much could be done until the 200-inch at Palomar became available.

Kuiper made some preliminary measures in 1949, using the 82-inch reflector at the McDonald Observatory in Texas, and obtained a value of 6,400 miles, though with a large possible error. This would make the mass about $\frac{8}{10}$ that of the Earth, so that the observed perturbations of Uranus and Neptune might just be accounted for, allowing for observational errors and a few coincidences.

In March 1950, twenty years after Tombaugh's original discovery, Humason and Kuiper, using the Palomar telescope, obtained the first measures which might be expected to be reliable. The results were startling. Pluto proved to have a diameter of only 3,600 miles – less than that of Mars, not much more than that of Neptune's satellite Triton. It was thus smaller than any other planet apart from Mercury.

Obviously, this threw the whole question wide open again. If it were a normal type of body, Pluto could have only one-tenth of the Earth's mass, so that its perturbations on Uranus and Neptune would be negligible. On the other hand, it was by these very perturbations that it had been tracked down – and it would be strange indeed if two eminent mathematicians could obtain independent, accurate results based upon data which were completely erroneous.

If we accept the Humason–Kuiper diameter measurements coupled with a mass sufficient to explain the perturbations, the density of Pluto will work out to about 12 times that of the Earth, or 60 times that of water. Here again we run into difficulties. Such an enormous density seems improbable, to put it mildly. If true, Pluto would be a most remarkable body, made up entirely of very heavy materials, and with a tremendous surface gravity – so that a man weighing 13 stone on Earth would weigh over 60 stone on Pluto! A pull of this kind would indicate a high escape velocity, and consequently an atmosphere made up of hydrogen or helium would be dense and low-lying, causing Pluto to reflect much of the feeble sunlight which falls on it. (Most gases, of course, would liquefy, since the aphelion temperature must be in the region of —400 degrees F.) Yet it is generally thought that Pluto's albedo, or reflecting power, is actually very low.

In every way the theory of excessive density seems to be unlikely; so is there any better solution to the problem?

One suggestion is that Pluto is really much larger than the diameter measures indicate. If it once had an atmosphere which cooled and froze, covering the surface with a smooth deposit, the planet would have a reflecting surface rather like that of a ball-bearing. Seen from a distance, it would show a bright patch near its centre corresponding to the reflection of the Sun, surrounded by a darker area. We would see only the bright patch, and might easily think that we were measuring the full diameter of the planet.

This idea seems to have been first proposed by A. C. D. Crommelin in 1936, and is at least plausible, though it is scarcely more than a guess. A variation of it is that Pluto contains seas – not of water, but of liquid methane, in which case the same effects would be seen.

Unless we regard the discovery of Pluto as a happy accident, we must accept a much higher mass than is indicated by the Humason–Kuiper measures of the planet's diameter. At present the problem remains unsolved. It is hopeless to try to observe any surface detail, as no ordinary telescope will show Pluto as much more than a faint yellowish speck of light, and we are unlikely to find out much more until the planet has been under observation for long enough to enable the real mass to be calculated with greater accuracy.

The one hope of doing this in the near future would be to discover a satellite. The pull of Pluto upon such an attendant would give us a reliable key to the whole problem. Unfortunately, even a large satellite would be very difficult to detect at so great a distance.

At present (1962) Pluto is still out beyond the orbit of Neptune, but it is drawing in to perihelion, and from 1969 to 2009 it will forfeit the title of 'the outermost planet'. It will be nearest to us in 1989, but subsequently it will retreat once more; by 2113 it will have reached perihelion, four and a half thousand million miles from the Sun. For fifty years or more on either side of that date it will be so dim that only giant telescopes will show it, and our great-great-grandchildren will find it no easy task to observe Pluto at all.

It would need an instrument much more powerful than the Palomar 200-inch reflector to show any surface details on Pluto. However, if the surface has light and darker areas, changes in the planet's apparent brightness might give some information as to the rotation period.

Delicate measures carried out in 1955 by M. F. Walker and R. Hardie, using the 42-inch reflector at Flagstaff, have indeed disclosed such variations. Combining their results with the earlier work of Walker in 1954, they have come to the conclusion that Pluto's rotation period is 6 days 9 hours. The changes in brightness are small, about the same as those of Mars for one rotation (approximately one-tenth of a star magnitude), and Walker and Hardie think that Pluto is at present seen more nearly with its equator towards us than pole-on.

Of course these results are tentative, but at least we have something to go on. It is rather strange to reflect that the determination of the rotation period of Pluto is probably more reliable than that of the nearest of the planets, Venus.

Pluto is so extraordinary a body, and so unlike any of the other planets, that it may not be a genuine planet at all, but merely a former satellite of Neptune which has been somehow torn free. This point of view has been supported by Kuiper and others, and seems reasonable enough, particularly since Pluto seems to be about the same size as the larger of Neptune's two remaining satellites. On thc other hand the theory is completely unproved, and it will be extremely difficult to come to a firm conclusion one way or the other.

Pluto is now considerably brighter than it was in 1930, when Tombaugh first identified it. It has been claimed that an 8-inch telescope will show it, and I have often seen it easily in my 12½-inch reflector, though it is of course hard to identify at a glance in view of the fact that it looks exactly like a faint star. Yet Plutonian astronomers – assuming that they could exist! – would have a very poor view of the rest of the planetary system. Neptune would be visible, and at times Uranus, but the Earth and its neighbours would never be seen. Pluto must be a dismal world; from it, even the Sun would appear as nothing but a tiny though brilliant disk.

The little we know about Pluto teaches us that it is the most desolate body in the Solar System. It can never have known the breath of life; it marks the frontier of the Sun's kingdom.

Chapter 16

Beyond the Planets

SO FAR AS WE know at present, Pluto – for most of its orbit – is the outermost planet of the Solar System. Beyond it there is a vast gap, containing nothing but the incredibly tenuous interstellar material and an uncertain number of comets.

When the distances of some of the stars were first measured, towards the middle of the last century, it was found that the distances involved were so great that our familiar unit, the mile, was hopelessly inconvenient. Instead, astronomers turned to the 'light-year', which is equivalent to rather less than six million million miles. Light takes only five and a half hours to travel out to Pluto, but over four years to reach us from the nearest star, so that our Solar System proves to be very insignificant in the universe as a whole.

There may well be another planet moving round the Sun beyond Pluto. If it exists, it must be very faint, and even if it is the size of Uranus and Neptune its discovery must be largely a matter of luck; still, it may be there. As we have seen, it may be wrong to regard Pluto as a proper planet at all. It may be an escaped satellite of Neptune, or even merely the brightest member of a ring of trans-Neptunian asteroids – in which case the true 'Planet X' of Lowell may still await discovery. What evidence have we either way?

Strangely enough, the strongest argument in favour of a trans-Plutonian planet is provided by those erratic wanderers, the comets. Comets are the stray members of the Solar System. Although sometimes of vast size, they are very flimsy and unsubstantial, made up chiefly of tiny solid particles[1] and very tenuous gas; their masses are negligible, less even than those of small satellites such as Phœbe and Nereid. Consequently, their orbits can be violently distorted by the action of the planets. A typical case was that of Lexell's Comet, which went so close to Jupiter that its whole orbit and revolution period was completely changed. Generally speaking, comets move

[1] It is now thought that these particles are, in the main, ices.

in paths which are much more eccentric than those of the planets, and it is a striking fact that over fifty of them have their aphelia (maximum distances from the Sun) at about the mean distance of Jupiter.

This is no mere coincidence. Jupiter's powerful pull is responsible, and to some extent the Giant Planet may be said to control its comet family. Saturn has a similar family of half a dozen comets, Uranus three, and Neptune at least eight. In 1928, Pickering pointed out that there were sixteen known comets with their aphelion distances at about 7,000 million miles from the Sun, and this seemed to him to indicate the presence of a massive, remote body which he named Planet P. He considered that it must be larger than Uranus or Neptune, and even went so far as to work out a preliminary orbit for it.

Following the discovery of Pluto in 1930, Pickering published a paper about his hypothetical Planet P, and wrote as follows:

> When I first recognized its importance, from its comets, I mentally reserved for it the name Pluto, as the son of Saturn and the brother of Jupiter and Neptune; but unfortunately that small object now known as Pluto came round and perturbed Neptune some ten years before the leisurely P arrived and perturbed Uranus, and so received the name. Pluto should be renamed Loki, the god of thieves! A suitable name for P will indeed be difficult to find when that planet is discovered.

Pickering was firmly convinced that Planet P really existed, and recently K. Schütte, of Munich, has returned to the problem and come to similar conclusions. A by-product of Schütte's investigations has been the recognition of a group of five comets whose aphelion distances show that they may form a Plutonian 'family', though owing to Pluto's peculiar orbit and small mass it is difficult to be at all certain.

If Pickering and Schütte are right, the new planet will probably be found one day. Unfortunately the comets give no clue as to where it may be in the sky, and short of a chance discovery the only course is to wait until the movements of Neptune and Pluto are known so accurately that we will be able to tell whether they are in fact being perturbed by a more remote body. We may have to wait for many years.

If Planet P exists, it will indeed be a twilight world. At a distance of 7,000 million miles the sunlight would be drastically reduced, and the Sun itself would appear so shrunken that to our eyes it would be nothing more than a bright point. No other planet could be made out, and any hypothetical inhabitant of Planet P might well imagine that his was the Sun's only attendant.

Yet we are being insular in our outlook. The Sun is an ordinary star, quite unremarkable in every way; it is of average mass and luminosity, and we would be most unwise to suppose that it is unique in having a retinue of planets. Let us examine the problem a little more closely.

In the first two chapters of this book, something was said about the system in which we live. This system, or Galaxy, is made up of about 100,000 million stars, of which the Sun is one. Many of these stars are very similar to the Sun in all respects, which is a significant point.

Beyond our system there are millions of other galaxies. One of the closest, the Great Spiral in Andromeda, can be seen with the naked eye as a faint, hazy patch of light, but since it is about 2,000,000 light-years away even our greatest telescope will show only the more luminous stars in it; a star no more powerful than the Sun would be quite undetectable. Therefore, it is quite hopeless even to think of searching for planets in other galaxies.

We need not be discouraged at this, since the Galaxy in which we are situated contains so many suns which might reasonably be expected to be the centres of planetary systems. Unfortunately there are a great many uncertain factors. Until we know just how the bodies of the Solar System were formed, it is hard to tell whether they would have come into being if the Sun had been a different sort of star. Yet the general argument is unaffected. The Sun is no freak; therefore the planets are presumably not freakish either.

The trouble is that we cannot hope to observe any planets which may be circling other stars simply because they will be too faint. A planet, remember, has no light of its own, and has to depend upon reflected glory. If Jupiter, the giant of the Solar System, happened to revolve round even the nearest star, it would be far beyond the range of the Palomar telescope. However, it might make its presence felt by its gravitational pull, and one of our stellar neighbours, 61 Cygni, does actually seem to have a massive planet moving round it.

61 Cygni – so called because it lies in the constellation of Cygnus, the Swan, and was No. 61 in a famous catalogue drawn up by Flamsteed – is visible to the naked eye, and became famous in 1838, when it became the first star to have its distance accurately measured. We now know that it is 11 light-years away, corresponding to over sixty million million miles, and that it is a twin system made up of two stars revolving round their common centre of gravity in about 700 years. The brighter component, A, has about $\frac{1}{19}$ of the Sun's luminosity, while the other component, B, is appreciably feebler.

In 1944 K. A. Strand announced that in addition to its orbital motion around the centre of gravity of the system, 61 Cygni B was 'wobbling' perceptibly in its path. The perturbing body could not be seen visually, it was much too faint for that; and since the 'wobble' was very small Strand deduced that the body must be of low mass. He worked out that it was only 15 times as massive as Jupiter.

Stars with masses as low as this do not exist; they can never have been formed, and therefore the disturbing body is not a true star. It may well be a non-luminous globe, depending for its light and heat entirely upon the feeble sun around which it moves. It may, of course, retain a certain amount of inherent light, but the evidence – uncertain though it is – seems to indicate that we are dealing with a planet and not a star.

A few other similar cases have been reported; in particular, the star 70 Ophiuchi may have a companion whose mass is only 12 times that of Jupiter. If so, it must certainly be planetary rather than stellar in nature.

Obviously, we cannot hope to detect any but very massive extra-solar planets. A smaller body the size of the Earth, or even Neptune, would produce no measurable perturbations upon even a relatively non-massive star. This must not be taken as evidence that planets of terrestrial dimensions are rare; on the contrary, they are probably very common.

It must be borne in mind, too, that our own Earth would be completely invisible to beings who lived in the system of (say) 61 Cygni, assuming that their scientific equipment were comparable with ours. Such beings could not possibly tell that an undistinguished yellow star rules a family of at least nine planets, one of which is inhabited by men who are almost ready to make their first journeys into space.

In short, there is strong indirect evidence that other planets, and other Earths, are widely scattered throughout the universe. Whether direct evidence will ever be obtained is, of course, quite another matter.

Chapter 17

Life on the Planets

WE KNOW THAT THE Sun is a normal star; yet from our own point of view, the Earth is not a normal planet. It is unique inasmuch as it is the only world in the Solar System upon which we could survive under natural conditions. Of the other planets, only Mars and Venus have relatively tolerable climates, and both these worlds have atmospheres which would be unbreathable to us.

Once again, however, we are being insular in our outlook. A polar bear would soon die if taken to the middle of the Sahara Desert, while a camel would be equally unable to cope with conditions in the Arctic Circle; each has adapted itself to its own particular surroundings. Is there any reason why beings on other planets should not have done the same?

Before coming to any definite conclusions, let us pause to consider just how living creatures are built up. We cannot say just what 'life' is; we cannot create it (though, unhappily, we can destroy it with alarming ease), and neither can we tell how the first primitive living organisms arose on Earth. We do know, however, that all living structures depend upon carbon, because atoms of carbon have a remarkable ability to build up complex atom-groups of the right type.

There are only 92 different kinds of atoms in the universe, and each is peculiar to its own *element*. Other elements have been manufactured in recent years, but they are unstable, and probably do not occur in nature, so that we can be sure that even the remotest stars are made up of substances familiar to us.[1] The only other atom which possesses something like the building power of carbon is the atom of silicon. All the rest are quite incapable of behaving in such

[1] Some people find it difficult to believe that every particle of matter in the universe is made up of combinations of only 92 elements, but we can draw an analogy from our everyday experience – the symphonies of Beethoven, the lyric dances of Grieg, the melodies of Sullivan, and even 'rock 'n roll' are all formed by different combinations of the twelve fundamental notes of the octave.

a way. This is not mere opinion; it is scientific fact, and mathematical analysis can prove it. It seems, therefore, that all living organisms in the universe must be based either upon carbon or else upon silicon.

Carbon-based life must be essentially similar to our own; there is no room for doubt upon that score. Silicon-based life does not occur on Earth, and if it occurs anywhere it is certainly of alien form. However, there is no evidence that it does exist, and there is a great deal of indirect evidence that it does not. In short, we are justified in supposing that all kinds of life in the universe are fundamentally similar to that which we know.

Naturally, life could well assume diverse forms. Yet this is the case also on Earth; there is not much superficial resemblance between (say) a man, a seal, a spider, and a jellyfish. The common factor is that all are carbon-based, which means that all require an equable temperature, a suitable atmosphere, and means of nourishment.

Of course, we may be entirely wrong. Somewhere out in the system of Sirius or 61 Cygni there may be a planet upon which live bright green men who coo like pigeons and are made of pure uranium – but it does not seem very likely, and we must make a reasonable interpretation of what evidence we can collect. 'Life', so far as we are concerned, must mean 'life as we know it'.

As we have seen, there may be many Solar Systems in the universe, some of them containing worlds which are almost replicas of the Earth. Life has arisen on our planet; therefore it will probably arise anywhere where conditions are similar, and may have developed to a stage far in advance of ours. In 1960, indeed, a team of United States scientists even tried to carry out a series of experiments which would have seemed fantastic only a few years ago. This was the famous 'Project Ozma'.

We know that there are vast clouds of rarefied hydrogen spread between the stars, and that these hydrogen atoms emit radiation on a wavelength of 21·1 centimetres. The 21-centimetre radiation can be collected by means of radio telescopes, and has given us invaluable information about the structure of the Galaxy. If there are other advanced beings in the star-system, they will presumably know all about the radio emissions, and will be keeping a watch upon that particular frequency. The idea behind Project Ozma was to detect signals on the 21-centimetre frequency which were non-natural, and which could therefore be interpreted as attempts by other beings to 'call up'. Of the stars within a dozen light years of us, there are two – Tau Ceti and Epsilon Eridani – which are not totally unlike the Sun, and so might reasonably be expected to possess planetary systems; therefore these two stars were selected for the main investigation.

It is hardly necessary to add that Project Ozma was 'the longest of long shots', and whether it was worth all the effort is debatable. No positive results were secured, and the experiment has now been discontinued.

Coming back to the Solar System, we must look for a world which is neither too hot nor too cold; where there is a tolerable atmosphere, and (of course) a suitably solid surface. The Earth fulfils all these requirements. What of the rest?

Most of the planets are ruled out at once on the grounds of temperature. Jupiter and the other giants, as well as Pluto, are too cold; Mercury too hot on one side and too cold on the other – though there may be a loophole here if we remember the 'twilight zone' between the two extreme regions. Excessive heat breaks up the carbon-based molecules and destroys all living cells, while excessive cold is equally effective at destroying the vital force. If we add Mercury to our list of rejects on the score of virtual 'airlessness', we come back, as always, to Venus and Mars.

Our ideas have developed very rapidly during the last hundred and fifty years. It is surprising to learn that Sir William Herschel, discoverer of Uranus and first president of the Royal Astronomical Society, was quite convinced that there were people living in a warm, comfortable region beneath the surface of the Sun.[1] We now know, however, that the intense solar heat breaks up not only the delicate, complex molecules, but also atomic groups which are capable of resisting temperatures which to us would be intolerable. Only Mars and Venus, in the Solar System, have climates which are even remotely suitable for life.

It seems overwhelmingly probable that living organisms exist on

[1] Ideas of this sort still linger on. In 1953 there was a lawsuit between a German scientific society and a solicitor named Büren, who argued that the Sun was habitable and had vegetation on it. The legal court at Osnabrück decided in favour of the Society, but failed to persuade Herr Büren that his ideas were somewhat out of date! Conversely, a British clergyman has recently published a booklet proving conclusively that the Sun is cold.

Mars, and are responsible for the famous dark areas. Moreover, laboratory experiments have shown that certain lowly Earth-type organisms could survive under Martian conditions. Work along these lines has been carried out in America and in Russia, and in 1960 I suggested doing the same sort of thing in England. The actual experiments have been made by F. L. Jackson at King's College Hospital, and have yielded interesting results.

Our aim was to simulate Martian conditions as closely as possible. Nothing could be done about the difference in gravity, but this did not seem to invalidate the experiment. Special containers were made, and provided with an atmosphere of the correct Martian density and composition, assuming the correctness of the data given by de Vaucouleurs. Suitable 'soils' were provided, and provision made for the appropriate temperature variations. As expected, plants such as cacti died at once; they could not endure the conditions, and a single 'Martian night' was fatal to them. Neither did microscopic animals survive. Bacteria cultures, however, proved to be more adaptable, and some of them appeared to be able not only to live, but also to multiply to some extent. Limonite, widely believed to cover much of Mars, discouraged some of the bacteria, but others tolerated it better.

These results are preliminary only – the work is still going on – and in any case they do not prove that living organisms actually do exist on Mars or anywhere else. All they show is that a Martian environment is not necessarily fatal to all living organisms of the sort known to us.

Moreover, it must be admitted that there is no absolute proof of the absence of all animal life on Mars and Venus. We may consider it unlikely, but we cannot reject it out of hand. When we turn to 'men', however, the situation is very different.

Many millions of years ago, Mars may well have been a world with a dense atmosphere and abundant moisture. It has therefore been suggested that as the atmosphere leaked away into space and the oceans dried up, the 'Martians' were able to adapt themselves to the changing conditions. This is a fascinating theory, but we have to admit that it is depressingly improbable. Venus, on the other hand, may be a world upon which life is just beginning – and may eventually develop, provided that we ourselves do not go there and interfere with it (which is perfectly possible).

It would be interesting to try to communicate with our hypothetical Martians. A scheme was once proposed for tracing out vast geometrical designs in the Sahara Desert in the hope that the Martians would see them and reply in similar vein; after all, they have plenty of deserts, and geometrical designs must be universal. Professor Lancelot Hogben has even worked out a possible means of making the Martians understand us when we first meet. Frequent attempts have also been made to call up Mars by radio, but so far the beings on the Red Planet have not been courteous enough to reply, which indicates either that they do not exist, that their wireless is not sufficiently advanced to pick up the messages, or that they know enough about us to keep us at a safe distance!

Conversely, it has been maintained that beings from other worlds are in the habit of paying visits to Earth. Not long ago, a Russian 'scientist' suggested that the Siberian meteorite of 1908 was no meteorite at all, but a grounded space-ship which exploded. We have also had the flying saucer craze, which began in 1947 and is not quite defunct even yet, since saucer enthusiasts still hold meetings, publish magazines, and hint gloomily that The Authorities are sparing no effort to conceal the great truth. Eccentricity of this sort is quite harmless, and is often entertaining; but it is not science.

Lastly, what of the future?

Though we seem to be alone in the Solar System, there is every hope that men will be able to reach other worlds before many years have passed by. The problems of true interplanetary flight cannot be discussed in a few lines, and much work remains to be done before the first space voyages can take place; but we need not be discouraged, for we, too, can play our part in the great adventure which is to come. Our task is to find out as much as we can about the worlds we hope to explore. The tiny disks of the planets, shining into our telescopes across millions of miles of space, throw down a challenge to us; they give us the hope of a key to their secrets. If we can solve at least some of the outstanding problems, we will be doing much to help those descendants of ours who will eventually push the frontiers of Earth far into the void.

Appendix I

Observing the Planets

A GREAT DEAL OF pleasure can be had from studying the night skies with binoculars, or with an ordinary naval telescope. For serious work on the planets, however, a proper astronomical instrument is naturally essential, and telescopes are expensive. Fortunately there are ways and means round this difficulty.

Telescopes are of two kinds: refractors and reflectors. Each type has its own advantages and disadvantages. The refractor is employed for ordinary terrestrial use, and is therefore more familiar; it collects its light by means of a lens or *object-glass*, which brings the light to focus near the bottom of the tube, forming an image which is magnified by a second lens – or, more correctly, a combination of lenses – known as an eyepiece. Astronomical refractors differ from terrestrial ones in an important respect; they give an inverted image, because the extra lenses put into the naval telescope to correct for this are left out. Each time a ray of light passes through a lens it becomes slightly enfeebled, and though this is of no importance in everyday use it is very important indeed when studying a faint celestial body from which every scrap of available light must be utilized. All astronomical pictures and diagrams are thus oriented with the south at the top.

The reflector dispenses with the object-glass, and collects its light by means of a suitably shaped mirror. In the usual form, invented by Sir Isaac Newton and therefore known as the Newtonian, the light passes unchecked down the tube – which may be a skeleton, not a closed tube at all – and falls upon the mirror at the bottom. The light-rays are then reflected back up the tube and concentrated upon a smaller mirror near the upper end. This smaller mirror, or *flat*, is tilted at an angle of 45 degrees, and directs the light-rays to the side of the tube, where an image is formed and magnified by an eyepiece in the usual way.

There have been many arguments about the relative merits of

refractors and reflectors. Reflectors are cheaper, and more comfortable to use; moreover they can be made by any reasonably skilful amateur, whereas lens-making is beyond any but the experienced professional. On the other hand, reflectors are more trouble, as they need a good deal of adjustment and the mirrors require periodical attention.

The resolving ability of a telescope is determined by the diameter of the object-glass (for a refractor) or main mirror (for a reflector). Inch for inch, the lens is the more effective. A 3-inch refractor will be found adequate for some useful work, at least on the Moon, and is the beginner's favourite instrument; but no reflector of under 6 inches aperture is of much real use, though it will show some pretty sights.

Trouble is often experienced because of poor mounting. Many small refractors are sold on table 'pillar and claw' stands, which look nice and are cheap, but are unfortunately quite useless. They can never be made properly steady, and a telescope which quivers at the lightest footfall or breath of wind will produce a planetary image which seems to dance a wild waltz in the heavens.

If you buy a refractor on a pillar and claw, the best course is to consign the mounting to the dustbin and invest in a tripod. A heavy wooden camera tripod will do quite well, and will provide the stability needed. Reflectors are not quite so easy to mount, but present no real difficulties.

In general, refractors over 4 inches aperture and reflectors over 6 inches need a permanent mount, preferably something in the nature of a concrete pillar; but this is not a hard-and-fast rule, and some larger telescopes, particularly reflectors, may be made reasonably portable.

Mounting the telescope equatorially, i.e. on a revolving axis directed towards the celestial pole, is a great help; and well-equipped observatories have their telescopes fitted with clock drives to move the instruments and compensate for the rotation of the Earth. A simpler alternative is to have manual slow motions – rods which may be twisted to move the telescope very slightly. Even these, however, are not strictly necessary for small telescopes such as 3-inch refractors.

The usual obstacle to a permanent observing site is lack of sky-space. It nearly always happens that an inconvenient tree or house is so placed that it covers a vital area. A small tree or bush can often be reduced or eliminated by judicious (sometimes surreptitious) chopping, but a massive oak is another matter, while even the most enthusiastic amateur is apt to have qualms about removing the top storey of his house. If a permanent site has to be selected from a number of unprepossessing possibilities, it is best to retain as much of the southern sky as possible. Planets are best placed when southerly, as they are then at their highest, and it is useless to observe a planet when it is low down near the horizon. This applies equally to Mercury and Venus, which must be regarded as daytime objects.

It often happens that the beginner buys a small refractor on a pillar and claw stand, perches it precariously upon a rickety table, pokes it out of (or through) a window, and hopes to see something startling, such as a Martian canal. He will be disappointed. Turbulence due to the meeting of the warm air indoors and the cooler air outdoors is invariably sufficient to disturb the image so much that nothing will be seen except a shimmering, shapeless blob of light. Moreover, only an expert contortionist could find a comfortable observing attitude with his telescope aimed through a window, and altogether the procedure is not to be recommended.

Meteorological conditions are all-important. Many people are surprised when they first learn that no optical telescope can penetrate cloud; indeed, the thinnest cloud-layer is usually fatal to the sharpness and steadiness of a planetary image. Thin mist, however, is not so disastrous. Misty conditions are often accompanied by steadiness of the atmosphere, and good results can be obtained on bright objects, though anything in the nature of real fog is naturally hopeless. On the other hand, very brilliant starlight nights often prove to be of no use, with images flickering about and every evidence of marked turbulence in the upper air.

In addition to a good telescope, it is essential to have good eyepieces. Using a good instrument with a poor eyepiece is like using a good record-player with a blunt needle, and this important fact is sometimes overlooked.

Eyepieces are of different kinds, and will give different magnifications. Fortunately they are made so that any eyepiece will fit any telescope (theoretically, at least!), and so buying a new telescope does not involve buying a new set of eyepieces. For a 3-inch refractor, it is advisable to have several eyepieces: one giving low magnification (30 to 40 diameters) for general views, another (80 to 120) for normal drawing of planetary details, another (120 to 150) for use on good nights, and yet another (180 to 200) for use under conditions of exceptionally good seeing. However, it is a grave mistake to try to use too high a power. A smallish, sharp image will reveal more detail than a larger but diffuse one, and the slightest blurring should be the signal to change to a lower magnification.

With greater apertures, higher magnifications can of course be used consistently. On my 8½-inch reflector I generally work at powers of between 200 and 400; on my 12½-inch reflector, anything between 250 and 600, though it is not often that conditions in south England will permit a magnification in excess of about 450.

Experience with giant telescopes has shown me that sharpness is much more important, in the long run, than pure magnification. Powers of around 400 used on the Meudon 33-inch refractor showed far more detail than could be seen with greater magnification on smaller telescopes. The golden rule should be: Use the highest power which will give a really clear, steady image. Do not tolerate the slightest blurring. If even a lower power will not give good results, there is obviously something wrong with the atmospheric conditions, and the only answer is to give up altogether until things improve.

Above all – never place any reliance upon an observation made hastily or under poor conditions. Such work is not only useless, but is actually misleading. One good observation is worth more than a thousand fairly good ones.

Appendix II

Useful Work for the Amateur

MERCURY

FOR MERCURY, IT MUST be admitted that little useful work can be done without large telescopes, but it is always a source of satisfaction to catch sight of the elusive little planet and to watch its phases. Occasionally, definite markings can be made out with modest apertures; I have seen the Solitudo Criophori with my 6-inch reflector. The main trouble about observing Mercury is that unless it can be located in broad daylight, which is virtually impossible unless the telescope is equipped with setting circles and clock, it has to be observed when low in the sky, so that its light is coming through the full thickness of our atmosphere and the definition suffers.

VENUS

Despite the general paucity of detail, Venus is a worth-while object to observe. The main points to be looked for are as follows:

(*a*) Phase. It is desirable to note the exact time of dichotomy, since, as has been explained, theory and observation generally disagree. There may be similar discrepancies at other conditions of phase.

(*b*) The shadings, which should be drawn as definitely as possible.

(*c*) The brighter areas, including the persistent cusp-caps.

(*d*) Any irregularities in the terminator.

(*e*) Any sign of the Ashen Light. For this, it is essential to block out the bright crescent by some sort of device fitted in the eyepiece.

Venus, however, is a difficult object to study. When it is a brilliant object in the evening or morning sky its image is bound to be unsteady, and one must be wary of atmospheric effects; for instance, the oft-recorded serrated edge of the planet's terminator is due to this cause. It is seldom that a really high magnification can be used.

Apart from Ashen Light studies the only reliable method is to observe in full daylight.

Venus appears much larger in the crescent stage than when half or gibbous, but generally speaking it is best to make all drawings the same size. A diameter of 2 inches to the full circle is recommended.

THE MOON

There is so much to see on the Moon, and so much work open to even the modestly equipped observer, that it is impossible to give an adequate summary in a few paragraphs. (Further details will be found in my *Guide to the Moon.*) However, a few hints may be given.

First, one must learn to find one's way about the lunar surface. My own method was to take a notebook and allot one page to each formation named in Elger's outline map. Within eighteen months or so, I had secured at least two drawings of each formation – rough in many cases, but enough to enable me to recognize the craters again. The time and trouble taken proved to be well worth while in the end.

Ordinarily, a lunar feature is most conspicuous when seen near the terminator, as the heights are then revealed by their shadows. Even a great crater such as Ptolemæus becomes obscure when seen under a high light.

To begin a lunar sketch, first select the formation to be drawn, and survey it carefully. Then draw in the main shapes (unless you are using a photographic outline), putting in shadows and coarser details. Next change to a higher power, and insert smaller details, afterwards checking everything to make sure that there is no chance of error.

'Finished' shaded drawings are made by those who possess artistic skill; those who do not, such as myself, are better advised to keep to line drawings, which can be made just as accurate, though less pleasing to the eye. If a rough sketch is made at the telescope and later transferred into the observing log, the final result should be checked again at the telescope to make sure that there are no mistakes in interpretation.

Do not use too small a scale. Twenty miles to the inch is convenient. A drawing of a large area such as the complete Mare Imbrium drawn to a small scale is quite useless. A large crater such as Plato should be drawn with a major axis of something like 3 inches.

Of course, straightforward drawing of lunar craters and other features is of limited value, though it is instructive. When the observer has found his way about, he will be ready to start more serious work – for instance charting of the limb regions, searching for special objects such as domes, studying the bright ray-systems, or perhaps estimating the shadow-lengths inside small craters so that the heights of the walls above the floor can be worked out.

MARS

Mars is rather a difficult object for a small aperture. It comes to opposition only every other year, and in general it is only possible to make useful observations of it for a month or so on either side of the opposition date. However, a small telescope will show considerable detail, and valuable work can be carried out with instruments of over 6 inches aperture.

Owing to the smallness of the disk, Mars is the one planet on which a really high power should be used whenever possible. It is best to select a definite scale for the drawings (preferably 2 inches to the planet's diameter), and the phase, which is often considerable, should never be neglected. This can be worked out beforehand from yearly tables, and the disk outline prepared accordingly.

Before starting to draw Mars, it is wise to spend some time in surveying the planet, until the eye has become thoroughly adapted. When the drawing is begun, the polar cap and main dark areas should be sketched in as quickly as is compatible with accuracy, as Mars is rotating on its axis and there is a slow but perceptible drift of the markings across the disk. Minor detail can then be added at leisure. When the drawing is complete, and you are satisfied that nothing has been missed, written notes should be added about colours, intensities, and any special features such as clouds.

Do not expect to see too much. At first you may be able to make out nothing apart from a few dark areas and the white polar cap; but as you gain experience, you will see more and more.

THE MINOR PLANETS

Here, the main interest for the amateur lies in identifying the minor planets and following their movements from night to night. One

(Vesta) can sometimes be seen with the naked eye, and several more are within the range of binoculars and small telescopes. Their positions can be found from the Handbook of the British Astronomical Association together with a star atlas (Norton's is the best), and with a little practice they may be recognized quite easily.

JUPITER

It is no exaggeration to say that most of our knowledge of Jupiter's surface features is due to amateur astronomers. The disk of the Giant Planet abounds in detail, and a modest aperture of 6 inches or so is enough for really useful work to be done.

Disk drawings should be made as quickly as possible, as the rate of spin is rapid and the drift of the markings is very obvious. A drawing should be completed within ten minutes at most with regard to major details (minor ones can be filled in most slowly, without altering the general framework). The colours seen should then be noted, and also the relative intensities of the various zones.

A very important part of the Jupiter programme is the taking of 'transits'. A feature 'transits' when it passes across the central meridian, i.e. the line passing through the two poles and the centre of the disk. The polar flattening enables the central meridian to be found easily – and, incidentally, this flattening should never be neglected when a drawing is to be made; personally I use prepared printed disks.

Transit times should be estimated to the nearest minute, and accurate timing is essential. It might seem a difficult task to make the estimates with sufficient precision, but it becomes strangely easy with a little practice, and it is possible to take many transits in the course of an hour or so as the markings drift steadily across the yellowish Jovian disk.

These transits are important because they allow the longitude of the feature concerned to be calculated, and hence enable rotation periods to be derived. As has been shown, these periods are of particular interest to radio astronomers. It is easy to work out the longitude of the feature from the tables in the Handbook of the British Astronomical Association, which give the longitude of the central meridian for every hour; the only arithmetic involved is simple addition.

As the equatorial zone (System I) rotates more quickly than the rest of the planet (System II), two sets of tables are necessary, and there must be no confusion as to which set is to be used – otherwise the results will be most peculiar. (Remember that System I is bounded by the northern edge of the South Equatorial Belt and the southern edge of the North Equatorial Belt.) It is also necessary to indicate the part of the belt in which the feature lies; for instance, NEB(s) indicates 'the southern part of the North Equatorial Belt'. The usual abbreviations are: P = polar, T = temperate, E = equatorial, B = belt, Z = zone, D = disturbance, RS = Red Spot, pr = preceding, f = following.

It may also be useful to give an extract from my own observation book for one particular night:

1958 May 27. Conditions fair, but some unsteadiness. 12½ in. reflector, ×350. Some details in the EZ, and the NEB is decidedly double; slight brownish cast. The RS is pinkish. The SEB is discontinuous, but generally more prominent than the STB. The SSTB was seen. Drawing commenced at 21.55, finished at 22.04.

Transits:

		Longitude	
G.M.T.	*Feature*	*System I*	*System II*
21.59	Centre of hollow, NEB(s)	291·1	
22.00	Slight break in SEB(n)		275·0
22.04	Pr. of darker section of NEB(n)		277·4
22.05	Middle of streak crossing EZ	294·8	
22.09	Pr. part of darker area in SEB(n)		280·4
22.14	Pr. of darker area in NEB(s)	300·3	
	(Interruption from clouds, 22.16 – 22.33)		
22.35	F. end of broader section, SEB(n)		296·1
22.40	F. end of visible part of SEB(s)		299·1
22.47	Centre of hollow, NEB(s)	320·4	
	(Failure of definition, 22.49 – 23.02)		
23.09	Centre of RS		316·6
23.18	Pr. of broader section, SEB(n)		322·0
23.20	F. end of RS		323·2
23.25	Slight depression, NEB(s)	343·6	
23.29	Hollow, NEB(n)		328·6

At this period Jupiter was not particularly active, but it often happens that 40 or 50 transits can be taken in a period of a few hours. It is these observations which will eventually lead us to a better understanding of how the planet is constituted.

Surface details on the Galilean satellites cannot be made out except with very large telescopes, but estimates of relative brilliancies are of value – if three or more satellites are visible at the same moment.

It is also useful to make careful observations of the times of occurrence of the satellite phenomena – transits across the Jovian disk, shadow transits, occultations, and eclipses – whenever possible; these observations help in improving our knowledge of the motions of the satellites.

SATURN

Saturn is in some ways a convenient planet. It bears high powers well, even better than Jupiter; and although there is not generally much surface detail, there is always the chance of making a startling discovery – as W. T. Hay did on 1933 August 3, when he detected the famous white spot.

The paucity of well-defined detail means that transits are difficult to take, but whenever possible they should be observed in the same way as those on Jupiter. For this work, a telescope of at least 10 inches aperture is desirable. It is also valuable to estimate the colours and intensities of the various zones of the planet, as marked and so far unexplained changes occur from time to time.

Cassini's Division is an easy object when the rings are fairly open, but Encke's is elusive and should be carefully looked for. Attention should also be paid to the reported minor divisions, though, as has been shown, their real existence is doubtful. The Crêpe Ring has been suspected of variations in brilliancy, and it is worth searching for the oft-recorded but so far unconfirmed dusky ring outside Ring A. Estimate the colours and intensities of the rings, comparing them with each other and also with the disk, and using a scale of from 0 (white) to 10 (black shadow). When a drawing is being made, take great care to put in the shadows (rings on disk, disk on rings) accurately.

Occasionally Saturn passes in front of a star, and this is an important event, since it enables the transparencies of the various rings to be determined.

Any 3-inch refractor will show Titan, and with my 12½-inch reflector I have managed to see all the satellites apart from Phœbe.

It is important to estimate the relative magnitudes of the satellites; Iapetus is particularly interesting in this respect.

URANUS

No surface details can be seen with most amateur-owned telescopes, but it is useful to estimate the brightness of the planet, which seems to show curious fluctuations.

The path of Uranus among the stars is given for each year in the Handbook of the British Astronomical Association, and the stars suitable for comparison are given together with their magnitudes. All that need be done is to identify Uranus in its star-field, and then check its magnitude against a star whose brilliancy is known. A fairly low power is advisable.

NEPTUNE

Neptune may be found with a small telescope, but no surface features can be seen. Its brilliancy may be estimated in the same way as that of Uranus, though Neptune's magnitude appears to be comparatively steady.

PLUTO

Pluto can now be glimpsed with a moderate telescope, but it is difficult to identify, as it looks like a very faint star.

Lastly, it cannot be too strongly emphasized that each drawing should be accompanied by the following data: date, time (using the 24-hour clock, and never using Summer Time), name of observer, type and aperture of telescope, magnification, and conditions of seeing and transparency. If any of these facts are omitted, the drawing loses most or all of its value.

It will be seen from the above notes that the owner of an adequate telescope has a wide field of research open to him. No clear night, winter or summer, need be dull; the planets are always changing, and their moods, their caprices, their obstinate refusals to obey prediction, make them fascinating companions.

Of course, straightforward drawing of lunar craters and other features is of limited value, though it is instructive. When the observer has found his way about, he will be ready to start more serious work – for instance charting of the limb regions, searching for special objects such as domes, studying the bright ray-systems, or perhaps estimating the shadow-lengths inside small craters so that the heights of the walls above the floor can be worked out.

MARS

Mars is rather a difficult object for a small aperture. It comes to opposition only every other year, and in general it is only possible to make useful observations of it for a month or so on either side of the opposition date. However, a small telescope will show considerable detail, and valuable work can be carried out with instruments of over 6 inches aperture.

Owing to the smallness of the disk, Mars is the one planet on which a really high power should be used whenever possible. It is best to select a definite scale for the drawings (preferably 2 inches to the planet's diameter), and the phase, which is often considerable, should never be neglected. This can be worked out beforehand from yearly tables, and the disk outline prepared accordingly.

Before starting to draw Mars, it is wise to spend some time in surveying the planet, until the eye has become thoroughly adapted. When the drawing is begun, the polar cap and main dark areas should be sketched in as quickly as is compatible with accuracy, as Mars is rotating on its axis and there is a slow but perceptible drift of the markings across the disk. Minor detail can then be added at leisure. When the drawing is complete, and you are satisfied that nothing has been missed, written notes should be added about colours, intensities, and any special features such as clouds.

Do not expect to see too much. At first you may be able to make out nothing apart from a few dark areas and the white polar cap; but as you gain experience, you will see more and more.

THE MINOR PLANETS

Here, the main interest for the amateur lies in identifying the minor planets and following their movements from night to night. One

Appendix III

Astronomical Societies

ANY SERIOUS AMATEUR WILL be wise to join an astronomical society. The advantages gained will be manifold. He will receive the latest information, and will be put in touch with other observers; moreover he will receive help and advice if he needs it.

The leading amateur society in Britain is the British Astronomical Association, founded in 1890. There are special sections devoted to the planets: Mercury and Venus (director, Patrick Moore); Mars (E. H. Collinson); Jupiter (W. E. Fox), and Saturn (M. B. B. Heath). There is also a flourishing Lunar Section, directed by G. Fielder. These Sections issue Memoirs from time to time, and also publish their results in the Association's monthly Journal. The secretarial address of the Association is 303 Bath Road, Hounslow West, Middlesex.

A particularly active society in the United States is the Association of Lunar and Planetary Observers. Its periodical, *The Strolling Astronomer*, is edited by the Association's Founder, Prof. W. H. Haas (Pan-American College Observatory, Edinburg, Texas). The Secretary is David P. Barcroft, and the Counsellor is Dr. Lincoln La Paz, of the University of New Mexico. Special sections are devoted to Mercury (recorder, Geoffrey Gaherty); Venus (W. K. Hartmann); Mars (E. E. Both); Jupiter (P. R. Glaser); Saturn (Joel W. Goodman); Uranus and Neptune (L. B. Abbey) and the Moon (Leif J. Robinson and Clark R. Chapman). No specific qualification is needed for membership; all those who are interested in lunar and planetary astronomy are strongly recommended to join.

In Britain, the leading observational society is the British Astronomical Association (303 Bath Road, Hounslow West, Middlesex), where again there are special planetary sections. Of mainly professional societies, special mention should be made of the Astronomical Society of the Pacific, with headquarters in San Francisco; the bi-monthly Publications contain invaluable information. In Canada, the Royal Astronomical Society of Canada has various Centres, and publishes the regular Journal; it contains both professionals and amateurs. In the southern hemisphere, the Royal New Zealand Astronomical Society, the New South Wales Branch of the B.A.A., and the South African Astronomical Society carry out regular observational work.

Appendix IV

Planetary Literature

MANY BOOKS HAVE BEEN written about the planets, and the following list does not pretend to be at all complete; it contains only specialized works written in English, and which are still in print.

The Moon

FIELDER, G. *Structure of the Moon's Surface.* London, 1961
FIRSOFF, V. A. *Strange World of the Moon.* London, 1959
Surface of the Moon. London, 1961
MOORE, PATRICK. *Guide to the Moon.* London, 1957
WILKINS, H. P. *Our Moon.* London, 1959
and MOORE, PATRICK. *The Moon.* London 1961

Venus

MOORE, PATRICK. *The Planet Venus.* London, 1961

Mars

DE VAUCOULEURS, G. *The Planet Mars.* London, 1952
Physics of the Planet Mars. London, 1954
MOORE, PATRICK. *Guide to Mars.* London, 1960
STRUGHOLD, H. *The Green and Red Planet.* London, 1954

Jupiter

PEEK, B. M. *The Planet Jupiter.* London, 1958

Saturn

ALEXANDER, A. F. O'D. *The Planet Saturn.* London, 1962

General

JACKSON, F. L., and MOORE, PATRICK. *Life in the Universe.* London, 1962

SPENCER JONES, H. *Life on Other Worlds.* London, 1955
UREY, H. *The Planets.* Oxford, 1952
WHIPPLE, F. L. *Earth, Moon and Planets.* London, 1953

Of the numerous periodicals, special mention should be made of the monthly *Sky and Telescope* (Cambridge, Massachusetts) which is quite invaluable.

Appendix V

Tables of the Planets

Planet	Mean distance from the Sun, miles	Sidereal period	Axial rotation (equatorial)	Orbital eccentricity	Orbital inclination	Axial inclination, deg.	Mean orbital velocity, mi/sec.
Mercury	36,000,000	88 days	88 days	0·206	7° 00′	?	29·8
Venus	67,200,000	224·7 ,,	?	0·007	3° 24′	?	21·8
Earth	92,868,000	365 ,,	23h 56m	0·017	0°	23·5	18·5
Mars	141,500,000	687 ,,	24h 37m	0·093	1° 51′	25·2	15·0
Jupiter	483,300,000	11·86 years	9h 51m	0·048	1° 18′	3·1	8·1
Saturn	886,100,000	29·46 ,,	10h 14m	0·052	2° 29′	26·7	6·0
Uranus	1,783,000,000	84·01 ,,	10h 48m	0·044	0° 46′	98	4·2
Neptune	2,793,000,000	164·79 ,,	About 14h	0·007	1° 46′	29	3·4
Pluto	3,666,000,000	248·43 ,,	6d 9h	0·248	17° 10′	?	2·9

Planet	Equatorial diameter, miles	Oblateness	Mass (Earth=1)	Volume (Earth=1)	Density (Water=1)	Surface gravity (Earth=1)	Escape velocity, mi/sec.	Max. surface temperature, deg. F.
Mercury	2,900	0·0	0·05	0·06	5·1	0·37	2·6	+770
Venus	7,700	0·0	0·83	0·88	5·0	0·89	6·4	?
Earth	7,927	0·003	1	1	5·5	1	7·0	+140
Mars	4,200	0·005	0·11	0·15	4·1	0·39	3·2	+85
Jupiter	88,700	0·062	318	1312	1·3	2·54	37·1	−200
Saturn	75,100	0·096	95	763	0·7	1·13	22·0	−240
Uranus	29,300	0·06	15	50	1·7	1·09	13·9	−310
Neptune	27,700	0·02	17	43	2·2	1·41	15·5	−360
Pluto	3,600?	?	?	?	?	?	?	?

Tables of the Minor Planets

THE FIRST TEN MINOR PLANETS

Number and name	Year of discovery	Sidereal period, years	Mean distance from Sun, miles	Orbital inclination	Diameter, miles
1 Ceres	1801	4·60	257,000,000	10° 36′	427
2 Pallas	1802	4·61	257,400,000	34° 48′	280
3 Juno	1804	4·36	247,800,000	13° 00′	150
4 Vesta	1807	3·63	219,300,000	7° 08′	241
5 Astræa	1845	4·14	239,300,000	5° 20′	111
6 Hebe	1847	3·78	225,200,000	14° 45′	106
7 Iris	1847	3·68	221,500,000	5° 31′	93
8 Flora	1847	3·27	204,400,000	5° 54′	77
9 Metis	1848	3·69	221,700,000	5° 36′	135
10 Hygeia	1849	5·59	292,600,000	3° 49′	220

SOME OF THE EARTH-GRAZERS

Name	Year of discovery	Sidereal period, years	Orbital inclination, deg.	Orbital eccentricity
Eros	1898	1·76	10·8	0·22
Amor	1932	2·67	11·9	0·44
Apollo	1932	1·81	6·4	0·57
Adonis	1936	2·76	1·5	0·78
Hermes	1937	1·47	4·7	0·48
Icarus	1949	1·12	23·0	0·83

Tables of the Satellites

Satellite	Discoverer	Mean distance from centre of primary, miles	Period	Orbital eccentricity	Orbital inclination	Diameter, miles	Maximum magnitude
EARTH							
Moon	—	238,857	27d 7h 43m	0·055	5° 9′	2160	−12·5
MARS							
Phobos	Hall, 1877	5,800	7h 39m	0·017	2°	10	10
Deimos	Hall, 1877	14,600	1d 6h 18m	0·003	2°	5	11
JUPITER							
Amalthea	Barnard, 1892	113,000	11h 57m	0·003	0° 24′	150	13
Io	Galileo, 1610	262,000	1d 18h 28m	0·0	0°	2310	5·5
Europa	Galileo, 1610	417,000	3d 13h 14m	0·0	0°	1950	5·7
Ganymede	Galileo, 1610	666,000	7d 3h 43m	0·0	0°	3200	5·1
Callisto	Galileo, 1610	1,170,000	16d 16h 32m	0·0	0°	3220	5·8
VI (Hestia)	Perrine, 1904	7,120,000	250d 16h	0·158	27° 38′	100	13·7
VII (Hera)	Perrine, 1905	7,290,000	259d 16h	0·207	24° 46′	35	17
X (Demeter)	Nicolson, 1938	7,300,000	260d 12h	0·130	29° 01′	15	18·8
XII (Adrastea)	Nicolson, 1951	13,000,000	§625d	0·169	147°	14	18·9
XI (Pan)	Nicolson, 1938	14,000,000	§700d	0·207	164°	19	18·4
VIII (Poseidon)	Melotte, 1908	14,600,000	§739d	0·378	145°	35	16
IX (Hades)	Nicolson, 1914	14,700,000	§758d	0·275	153°	17	18·6

			SATURN				
Mimas	Herschel, 1789	115,000	22h 37m	0·020	1° 31′	300	12·1
Enceladus	Herschel, 1789	148,000	1d 08h 53m	0·004	0° 01′	400	11·6
Tethys	Cassini, 1684	183,000	1d 21h 18m	0	1° 06′	800	10·6
Dione	Cassini, 1684	234,000	2d 17h 41m	0·002	0° 01′	1000	10·7
Rhea	Cassini, 1672	327,000	4d 12h 25m	0·001	0° 21′	1100	9·7
Titan	Huygens, 1655	758,000	15d 22h 41m	0·029	0° 20′	3500	8·2
Hyperion	Bond, 1848	919,000	21d 6h 38m	0·104	0° 26′	200	13·0
Iapetus	Cassini, 1671	2,210,000	79d 7h 55m	0·028	14° 43′	2000 (?)	9
Phœbe	Pickering, 1898	8,040,000	§550d 9h	0·163	150°	150	14
			URANUS				
Miranda	Kuiper, 1948	80,700	1d 9h 56m	0·01	0°	200	17
Ariel	Lassell, 1851	119,000	2d 12h 29m	0·003	0°	1500	14
Umbriel	Lassell, 1851	266,000	4d 3h 28m	0·004	0°	800	14·7
Titania	Herschel, 1787	272,000	8d 16h 56m	0·002	0°	1500	14
Oberon	Herschel, 1787	364,000	13d 11h 7m	0·001	0°	1500	14
			NEPTUNE				
Triton	Lassell, 1846	219,000	§5d 21h 3m	0	159° 57′	3000 (?)	13
Nereid	Kuiper, 1949	3,450,000	359d	0·76	27° 27′	200	19·5

The diameters and magnitudes of the satellites of Uranus and Neptune are most uncertain, and this also applies to the diameters of the satellites of Saturn. Satellites marked § have retrograde motion. The five satellites of Uranus are also technically retrograde, owing to the fact that they revolve in the plane of the planet's equator, but are not generally reckoned as such.

Index